P9-CMQ-951

PATRIOTISM
PATRIOTISM
PATRIOTISM

PATRIOTISM
PATRIOTISM
PATRIOTISM

Selected by

Helen Hoke

Illustrated by

LEONARD EVERETT FISHER

Franklin Watts, Inc.
575 Lexington Avenue, New York 22

3961

ACKNOWLEDGMENTS

The selections reprinted in this book are used by permission and special arrangements with the proprietors of their respective copyrights, who are listed below. The compiler's and publisher's thanks to all who helped make this collection possible.

Anderson House for "Valley Forge," by Maxwell Anderson. Copyright 1934 by Maxwell Anderson. Copyright renewed 1962 by Gilda Anderson, Alan Anderson, Terence Anderson, Quentin Anderson, and Hesper A. Levenstein.

Appleton-Century-Crofts for "Oh Mother of a Mighty Race," by William Cullen Bryant. By permission of Appleton-Century-Crofts Trade Books, an affiliate of Meredith Press.

Boosey and Hawkes, Inc. for "Land of Hope and Glory," by Arthur C. Benson. Copyright 1902 by Boosey and Co., Ltd. Reprinted by permission.

Brandt and Brandt for "Written in a Time of Crisis," from *We Stand United and Other Radio Scripts*, by Stephen Vincent Benét. Published by Holt, Rinehart and Winston, Inc. Copyright 1941 by Stephen Vincent Benét.

Crown Publishers for "Up-Country," by Abioseh Nicol from *An African Treasury*, edited by Langston Hughes. Copyright 1960 by Langston Hughes. Reprinted by permission of Crown Publishers, Inc.

Dodd, Mead & Company for "The Soldier," by Rupert Brooke. Reprinted by permission of Dodd, Mead & Company from *The Collected Poems of Rupert Brooke*. Copyright 1915 by Dodd, Mead & Co. Copyright 1943 by Edward Marsh.

E. P. Dutton & Co. Inc. and Dutton Paperback Series for "The Trojan Women," by Euripides, translated by Robert Potter, from *The Spring of Civilization* by C. A. Robinson, Jr.

Miss Hazel Felleman, Hotel Beacon, 75th Street & Broadway, New York, N. Y., for "Land of the Free," by Arthur Nicholas Hosking, from *The Best Loved Poems of the American People*.

Charlie May Fletcher (Mrs. John Gould Fletcher) for "Lincoln," by John Gould Fletcher.

Harper & Row, Publishers for "Betty Zane," from *Boy's Book of Battle Lyrics*, by Thomas Dunn English. By permission of Harper & Row, Publishers.

To S.M., tiny in size, big in spirit, and, beginning as she did, wise in the knowledge of what love of country means.

ABOUT THIS BOOK

PATRIOTISM means, simply, love of country. The prose and poetry gathered together in this book express that love in various ways. At one extreme are the flowery tributes so popular a century or more ago. At the other extreme are the quiet but urgent voices of statesmen, teachers, and philosophers reminding their fellow citizens of their duty to uphold the ideals that made their country great. Between the two extremes are a number of national anthems, words of praise for great men, the retelling of heroic deeds, and restatements of national ideals.

Because this is an American book, most of the selections are American. These selections stress the things Americans hold most sacred—freedom, equality, justice for all, and brotherhood. And, lest any young reader be deluded into believing that these are strictly "made-in-America" commodities, the editor has included a number of excerpts from the writings of people of other lands, writings that stress precisely the same ideals upon which Americans founded their country.

Helen Hoke

I

O COUNTRY MINE!

[xiii]

II

A CLIMATE OF FREEDOM

III

THE PEOPLE SING

IV

SING OF THE BRAVE AND THE MIRACLES THEY WROUGHT

V

WITH MALICE TOWARD NONE

VI

LEST WE FORGET

I

O COUNTRY MINE!

MY NATIVE LAND
Sir Walter Scott
Scottish poet and novelist (1771–1832)

Breathes there a man with soul so dead,
Who never to himself hath said,
"This is my own, my native land!"
Whose heart hath ne'er within him burned
As home his footsteps he hath turned
From wandering on a foreign strand?
If such there breathe, go, mark him well:
For him no minstrel raptures swell;
High though his titles, proud his name,
Boundless his wealth as wish can claim;
Despite those titles, power and pelf,
The wretch, concentered all in self,
Living, shall forfeit all renown,
And, doubly dying, shall go down
To the vile dust from whence he sprung,
Unwept, unhonored, and unsung.

HOME AND COUNTRY

from *The Man Without a Country*

Edward Everett Hale (1822–1909)

"Youngster, let me show you what it is to be without a family, without a home, and without a country. And if you are ever tempted to say a word or do a thing that shall put a bar between you and your family, your home, and your country, pray God in His mercy to take you that instant home to His own heaven. Stick by your family, boy; forget you have a self, while you do everything for them. Think of your home, boy; write and send, and talk about it. Let it be nearer and nearer to your thought the farther you have to travel from it; and rush back to it when you are free. And for your country, boy, and for that flag, never dream a dream but of serving her as she bids you, though the service carry you through a thousand hells. No matter what happens to you, no matter who flatters you or who abuses you, never look at another flag, never let a night pass but you pray God to bless that flag. Remember, boy, that behind all these men you have to do with, behind officers, and government, and people even, there is the Country Herself, your Country, and that you belong to Her as you belong to your own mother. Stand by Her, boy, as you would stand by your mother!"

FOREFATHERS' SONG

Humorous invitation to new settlers to migrate to America
Written about 1630
Original manuscript in the hands of Massachusetts Historical
Collection

Author Unknown

New England's annoyances you that would know them,
Pray ponder these verses which briefly doth show them.
The place where we live is a wilderness wood,
Where grass is much wanting that's fruitful and good:
Our mountains and hills and our valleys below,
Being commonly covered with ice and with snow;
And when the northwest wind with violence blows,
Then every man pulls his cap over his nose:
But if any's so hardy and will it withstand,
He forfeits a finger, a foot or a hand.

But when Spring opens we then take the hoe,
And make the ground ready to plant and to sow;
Our corn being planted and seed being sown,
The worms destroy much before it is grown;
And when it is growing, some spoil there is made
By birds and by squirrels that pluck up the blade;
And when it is come to full corn in the ear,
It is often destroyed by raccoon and by deer.

And now all our garments begin to grow thin,
And wool is much wanted to card and to spin;
If we can get a garment to cover without,

[5]

Our other in-garments are clout upon clout.*
Our clothes we brought with us are apt to be torn,
They need to be clouted soon after they're worn,
But clouting our garments they hinder us nothing,
Clouts double are warmer than single whole clothing.

If fresh meat be wanting to fill up our dish,
We have carrots and turnips as much as we wish:
And if there's a mind for a delicate dish
We repair to the clam-banks and there we catch fish.
Instead of pottage and puddings and custards and pies,
Our pumpkins and parsnips are common supplies;
We have pumpkins at morning and pumpkins at noon,
If it was not for pumpkins we should be undone.

If barley be wanting to make into malt,
We must be contented, and think it no fault;
For we can make liquor to sweeten our lips,
Of pumpkins and parsnips and walnut-tree chips . . .

Now while some are going let others be coming,
For while liquor's boiling, it must have a scumming;
But I will not blame them, for birds of a feather
By seeking their fellows are flocking together.
But you whom the Lord intends hither to bring,
Forsake not the honey for fear of the sting;
But bring both a quiet and contented mind,
And all needful blessings you surely will find.

* patch upon patch

CENTENNIAL HYMN
John Pierpont (1785–1866)

Break forth in song, ye trees,
As through your tops the breeze
    Sweeps from the sea;
For on its rushing wings,
To your cool shades and springs,
That breeze a people brings,
    Exiled, though free.

Ye sister hills, lay down
Of ancient oaks your crown,
    In homage due;
These are the great of earth—
Great, not by kingly birth,
Great, in their well-proved worth,
    Firm hearts and true.

These are the living lights,
That, from your bold green heights,
    Shall shine afar,
Till they who name the name
Of Freedom, toward the flame
Come, as the Magi came
    Toward Bethlehem's star.

Gone are those great and good,
Who here, in peril stood

And raised their hymn.
Peace to the reverend dead!
The light, that on their head
Two hundred years have shed,
    Shall ne'er grow dim.

Ye temples, that, to God,
Rise where our fathers trod,
    Guard well your trust:
The faith, that dared the sea,
The truth, that made them free,
Their cherished purity,
    Their garnered dust.

Thou high and holy One,
Whose care for sire and son
    All nature fills,
While day shall break and close,
While night her crescent shows
O, let thy light repose
    On these our hills.

From THE BUILDING OF THE SHIP
Henry Wadsworth Longfellow (1807–1882)

Thou, too, sail on, O Ship of State!
Sail on, O UNION, strong and great!
Humanity with all its fears,
With all the hopes of future years,
Is hanging breathless on thy fate!
We know what Master laid thy keel,
What Workmen wrought thy ribs of steel,
Who made each mast, and sail, and rope,
What anvils rang, what hammers beat,
In what a forge and what a heat
Were shaped the anchors of thy hope!
Fear not each sudden sound and shock,
'Tis of the wave and not the rock;
'Tis but the flapping of the sail,
And not a rent made by the gale!
In spite of rock and tempest's roar,
In spite of false lights on the shore,
Sail on, nor fear to breast the sea!
Our hearts, our hopes, our prayers, our tears,
Our hearts, our hopes, our prayers, our tears,
Our faith triumphant o'er our fears,
Are all with thee—are all with thee!

OH MOTHER OF A MIGHTY RACE
William Cullen Bryant (1794–1878)

Oh mother of a mighty race,
Yet lovely in thy youthful grace!
The elder dames, thy haughty peers,
Admire and hate thy blooming years.
    With words of shame
And taunts of scorn they join thy name.

For on thy cheeks the glow is spread
That tints thy morning hills with red;
Thy step—the wild deer's rustling feet
Within thy woods are not more fleet;
    Thy hopeful eye
Is bright as thine own sunny sky.

Ay, let them rail—those haughty ones,
While safe thou dwellest with thy sons.
They do not know how loved thou art,
How many a fond and fearless heart
    Would rise to throw
Its life between thee and the foe.

They know not, in their hate and pride,
What virtues with thy children bide;
How true, how good, thy graceful maids
Make bright, like flowers, the valley-shades;
    What generous men
Spring, like thine oaks, by hill and glen;—

What cordial welcomes greet the guest
By thy lone rivers of the West.
How faith is kept, and truth revered,
And man is loved, and God is feared,
　　In woodland homes,
And where the ocean border foams.

There's freedom at thy gates and rest
For Earth's downtrodden and oppressed,
A shelter for the hunted head.
For the starved laborer toil and bread.
　　Power, at thy bounds,
Stops and calls back his baffled hounds.

Oh, fair young mother! on thy brow
Shall sit a nobler grace than now.
Deep in the brightness of the skies
The thronging years in glory rise.
　　And, as they fleet,
Drop strength and riches at thy feet.

THE FOURTH OF JULY
John Pierpont (1785–1866)

Day of glory! Welcome day!
Freedom's banners greet thy ray;
See! how cheerfully they play
   With thy morning breeze,
On the rocks where pilgrims kneeled,
On the heights where squadrons wheeled,
When a tyrant's thunder pealed
   O'er the trembling seas.

God of armies! did thy stars
On their courses smite his cars;
Blast his arm, and wrest his bars
   From the heaving tide?
On our standards! lo! they burn.
And, when days like this return,
Sparkle o'er the soldier's urn
   Who for freedom died.

God of peace! whose spirit fills
All the echoes of our hills,
All the murmur of our rills,
   Now the storm is o'er,
O let freemen be our sons,
And let future Washingtons
Rise, to lead their valiant ones
   Till there's war no more!

THE CONCORD HYMN
Ralph Waldo Emerson (1803–1882)

By the rude bridge that arched the flood,
Their flag to April's breeze unfurled,
Here once the embattled farmers stood,
And fired the shot heard round the world.

The foe long since in silence slept;
Alike the conqueror silent sleeps;
And Time the ruined bridge has swept
Down the dark stream which seaward creeps.

On this green bank, by this soft stream,
We set today a votive stone;
That memory may their dead redeem,
When, like our sires, our sons are gone.

Spirit, that made those spirits dare
To die, and leave their children free,
Bid Time and Nature gently spare
The shaft we raise to them and thee.

LAND OF THE FREE
Arthur Nicholas Hosking

America, O Power benign, great hearts revere your name,
You stretch your hand to every land, to weak and strong the same;
You claim no conquest of the sea, nor conquest of the field,
But conquest for the rights of man, that despots all shall yield.

  Chorus:
  America, fair land of mine, home of the just and true,
  All hail to thee, land of the free, and the Red-White-and-Blue.

America, staunch, undismayed, your spirit is our might:
No splendor falls on feudal walls upon your mountain's height,
But shafts of Justice pierce your skies to light the way for all,
A world's great brotherhood of man, that cannot, must not fall.

America, in God we trust, we fear no tyrant's horde:
There's light that leads toward better deeds than conquest by the
  sword;
Yet our cause is just, if fight we must until the world be free
Of every menace, breed, or caste that strikes at Liberty.

America, home of the brave, our song in praise we bring—
Where Stars and Stripes the winds unfurl, 'tis there that tributes
  ring;
Our fathers gave their lives that we should live in Freedom's
  light—
Our lives we consecrate to thee, our guide the Might of Right.

AMERICA

from *The National Ode, July 4, 1876*

Bayard Taylor (1825–1878)

Foreseen in the vision of sages,
    Foretold when martyrs bled,
She was born of the longing of ages,
    By the truth of the noble dead
    And the faith of the living fed!
No blood in her lightest veins
Frets at remembered chains,
Nor shame of bondage has bowed her head.
    In her form and features still
    The unblenching Puritan will,
    Cavalier honor, Huguenot grace,
    The Quaker truth and sweetness,
And the strength of the danger-girdled race
Of Holland, blend in a proud completeness.
From the homes of all, where her being began,
    She took what she gave to Man;
    Justice, that knew no station,
    Belief, as soul decreed,
    Free air for aspiration,
    Free force for independent deed!
    She takes, but to give again,
As the sea returns the rivers in rain;
And gathers the chosen of her seed
From the hunted of every crown and creed.
    Her Germany dwells by a gentler Rhine;

[15]

Her Ireland sees the old sunburst shine;
Her France pursues some dream divine;
Her Norway keeps his mountain pine;
Her Italy waits by the western brine;
　　And, broad-based under all,
Is planted England's oaken-hearted mood,
　　As rich in fortitude
As e'er went worldward from the island wall!
　　Fused in her candid light,
To one strong race all races here unite;
Tongues melt in hers, hereditary foemen
Forget their sword and slogan, kith and clan.
　　'Twas glory, once, to be a Roman:
She makes it glory, now, to be a man!

PLAIN CHANT FOR AMERICA
Katherine Garrison Chapin (189?–   )

For the dream unfinished
Out of which we came,
We stand together,
While a hemisphere darkens
And the nations flame.

Our earth has been hallowed
With death for freedom;
Our walls have been hallowed
With freedom's thought.

Concord, Valley Forge, Harpers Ferry
Light up with their flares
Our sky of doubt.

We fear tyranny as our hidden enemy:
The black-shirt cruelty, the goose-step mind.

No dark signs close the doors of our speaking,
No bayonets bar the door to our prayers,
No gun butts shadow our children's eyes.

If we have failed—lynchings in Georgia,
Justice in Massachusetts undone,
The bloody fields of South Chicago—
Still a voice from the bruised and the battered
Speaks out in the light of a free sun.

[17]

Saying, "Tell them again, say it, America;
Say it again till it splits their ears:
Freedom is salt in our blood and its bone shape;
If freedom fails, we'll fight for more freedom—
This is the land, and these are the years!
When freedom's a whisper above their ashes
An obsolete word cut on their graves.
When the mind has yielded its last resistance,
And the last free flag is under the waves—

"Let them remember that here on the western
Horizon a star, once acclaimed, has not set;
And the strength of a hope, and the shape of a vision
Died for and sung for and fought for,
And worked for,
Is living yet."

FREEDOM
Joel Barlow (1754–1812)

Sun of the moral world; effulgent source
Of man's best wisdom and his steadiest force,
Soul-searching Freedom! here assume thy stand,
And radiate hence to every distant land;
Point out and prove how all the scenes of strife,
The shock of states, the impassion'd broils of life,
Spring from unequal sway; and how they fly
Before the splendor of thy peaceful eye;
Unfold at last the genuine social plan,
The mind's full scope, the dignity of man,
Bold nature bursting through her long disguise,
And nations daring to be just and wise.
Yes! righteous Freedom, heaven and earth and sea
Yield or withhold their various gifts for thee;
Protected Industry beneath thy reign
Leads all the virtues in her filial train;
Courageous Probity, with brow serene,
And Temperance calm presents her placid mien;
Contentment, Moderation, Labor, Art,
Mold the new man and humanize his heart:
To public plenty private ease dilates,
Domestic peace to harmony of states.
Protected Industry, careering far,
Detects the cause and cures the rage of war,
And sweeps, with forceful arm, to their last graves,
Kings from the earth and pirates from the waves.

MY LAND
Thomas Osborne Davis (1814–1845)

She is a rich and rare land;
Oh! she's a fresh and fair land,
She is a dear and rare land—
  This native land of mine.

No men than hers are braver—
Her women's hearts ne'er waver;
I'd freely die to save her,
  And think my lot divine.

She's not a dull or cold land;
No! she's a warm and bold land;
Oh! she's a true and old land—
  This native land of mine.

Could beauty ever guard her,
And virtue still reward her,
No foe would cross her border—
  No friend within it pine.

Oh! she's a fresh and fair land,
Oh! she's a true and rare land!
Yes, she's a rare and fair land—
  This native land of mine.

THERE IS A LAND

James Montgomery
British poet (1771–1854)

There is a land, of every land the pride,
Beloved by Heaven o'er all the world beside;
Where brighter suns dispense serener light,
And milder moons imparadise the night:
A land of beauty, virtue, valor, truth,
Time-tutored age, and love-exalted youth.
Where shall that land, that spot of earth, be found?
Art thou a man? A patriot? look around!
O! thou shalt find, howe'er thy footsteps roam,
That land thy country, and that spot thy home.

HECUBA'S LAMENT

*The Trojan queen, carried off to Greece as a slave, laments the
destruction of her city.*

from *The Trojan Women*

Euripides

Greek dramatist, fifth century B.C.

O miserable me! This is the last,
This is the extreme bound of all my ills.
I from my city go; my city sinks
In flames. But haste, my aged foot, though weak,
That I may yet salute the wretched town:
O Troy, that once 'mongst the barbaric states
Stoodst high aspiring, thy illustrious name
Soon shalt thou lose, for thee the raging flames
Consume: and from our country us they lead,
Now lead us slaves. Ye gods! But why invoke
The gods? Invoked before, they did not hear.
But bear me, let me rush into the flames:
For this would be the greatest glory to me,
With thee my burning country now to die.

THIS SCEPTER'D ISLE

from speech by John of Gaunt, Duke of Lancaster, Act II,
Scene 1, of *King Richard II*

William Shakespeare

This royal throne of kings, this scepter'd isle
This earth of majesty, this seat of Mars,
This other Eden, demi-paradise;
This fortress built by Nature for herself
Against infection and the hand of war;
This happy breed of men, this little world;
This precious stone set in the silver sea,
Which serves it in the office of a wall,
Or as a moat defensive to a house,
Against the envy of less happier lands;
This blessed plot, this earth, this realm, this England,
This nurse, this teeming womb of royal kings,
Feared by their breed, and famous by their birth,
Renowned for their deeds as far from home,
For Christian service and true chivalry . . .

[23]

MY NATIVE ENGLISH

from the reply of Thomas Mowbray, Duke of Norfolk, to King
Richard II's sentence of banishment, from *King Richard II*, Act I,
Scene 3

William Shakespeare

A dearer merit, not so deep a maim
As to be cast forth in the common air,
Have I deserved at your highness' hands.
The language I have learned these forty years,
My native English, now I must forego:
And now my tongue's use is to me no more
Than an unstringed viol or a harp;
Or like a cunning instrument cased up,
Or, being open, put into his hands
That knows no touch to tune the harmony;
Within my mouth you have engoaled my tongue,
Doubly portcullised with my teeth and lips;
And dull, unfeeling, barren ignorance
Is made my gaoler to attend on me.
I am too old to fawn upon a nurse,
Too far in years to be a pupil now:
What is thy sentence, then, but speechless death,
Which robs my tongue from breathing native air?

AMERICA FOR ME
Henry Van Dyke (1852–1933)

'Tis fine to see the Old World, and travel up and down
Among the famous palaces and cities of renown,
To admire the crumbly castles and the statues of the kings—
But now I think I've had enough of antiquated things.

So it's home again, and home again, America for me!
My heart is turning home again, and there I long to be
In the land of youth and freedom beyond the ocean bars,
Where the air is full of sunlight and the flag is full of stars.

Oh, London is a man's town, there's power in the air;
And Paris is a woman's town, with flowers in her hair;
And it's sweet to dream in Venice, and it's great to study Rome,
But when it comes to living, there is no place like home.

I like the German fir-woods, in green battalions drilled;
I like the gardens of Versailles with flashing fountains filled;
But, oh, to take your hand, my dear, and ramble for a day
In the friendly western woodland where Nature has her way!

I know that Europe's wonderful, yet something seems to lack!
The Past is too much with her, and the people looking back.
But the glory of the Present is to make the Future free—
We love our land for what she is and what she is to be.

[25]

Oh, it's home again, and home again, America for me!
I want a ship that's westward bound to plow the rolling sea.
To the blessed Land of Room Enough beyond the ocean bars,
Where the air is full of sunlight and the flag is full of stars.

THE SOLDIER
Rupert Brooke (1887–1915)

If I should die, think only this of me:
That there's some corner of a foreign field
That is forever England. There shall be
In that rich earth a richer dust concealed;
A dust whom England bore, shaped, made aware,
Gave, once, her flowers to love, her ways to roam;
A body of England's, breathing English air,
Washed by the rivers, blest by suns of home.
And think, this heart, all evil shed away,
A pulse in the eternal mind, no less
Gives somewhere back the thoughts by England given;
Her sights and sounds; dreams happy as her day;
And laughter, learnt of friends; and gentleness,
In hearts at peace, under an English heaven.

I AM AN AMERICAN
Elias Lieberman

I am an American.
My father belongs to the Sons of the Revolution;
My mother, to the Colonial Dames.
One of my ancestors pitched tea overboard in Boston Harbor;
Another stood his ground with Warren;
Another hungered with Washington at Valley Forge.
My forefathers were America in the making:
They spoke in her council halls;
They died on her battlefields;
They commanded her ships;
They cleared her forests.
Dawns reddened and paled.
Stanch hearts of mine beat fast at each new star
In the nation's flag.
Keen eyes of mine foresaw her greater glory:
The sweep of her seas,
The plenty of her plains,
The man-hives in her billion-wired cities.
Every drop of blood in me holds a heritage of patriotism
I am proud of my past.
I am an American.

I am an American.
My father was an atom of dust,
My mother a straw in the wind,
To his serene majesty.

One of my ancestors died in the mines of Siberia;
Another was crippled for life by twenty blows of the *knout*.
Another was killed defending his home during the massacres.
The history of my ancestors is a trail of blood
To the palace-gate of the Great White Czar.
But then the dream came—
The dream of America.
In the light of the Liberty torch
The atom of dust became a man
And the straw in the wind became a woman
For the first time.
"See," said my father, pointing to the flag that fluttered near,
"That flag of stars and stripes is yours;
It is the emblem of the promised land.
It means, my son, the hope of humanity.
Live for it—die for it!"
Under the open sky of my new country I swore to do so;
And every drop of blood in me will keep that vow.
I am proud of my future.
I am an American.

UP-COUNTRY
Abioseh Nicol

Then I came back
Sailing down the Guinea coast,
Loving the sophistication
Of your brave new cities:
Dakar, Accra, Cotonou,
Lagos, Bathurst, and Bissau,
Freetown, Libreville.
Freedom is really in the mind.

Go up-country, they said,
To see the real Africa.
For whosoever you may be,
That is where you come from.
Go for bush—inside the bush
You will find your hidden heart,
Your mute ancestral spirit.

And so I went,
Dancing on my way.

THE GIFT OUTRIGHT
Robert Frost (1875–1963)

The land was ours before we were the land's.
She was our land more than a hundred years
Before we were her people. She was ours
In Massachusetts, in Virginia;
But we were England's, still colonials,
Possessing what we still were unpossessed by,
Possessed by what we now no more possessed.
Something we were withholding made us weak
Until we found out that it was ourselves
We were withholding from our land of living,
And forthwith found salvation in surrender.
Such as we were we gave ourselves outright
(The deed of gift was many deeds of war)
To the land vaguely realizing westward,
But still unstoried, artless, unenhanced,
Such as she was, such as she would become.

II

A CLIMATE OF FREEDOM

EXCERPTS FROM THE MAGNA CARTA

[Ch. I]. We have granted also, and given to all the Freemen of our realm, for Us and for our Heirs forever, those Liberties underwritten, to have and to hold, to them and their Heirs forever.

[Ch. IX]. The City of London shall have all the old Liberties and Customs which it hath been used to have. Moreover, we will and grant that all other Cities and Boroughs, Towns, and the Barons of the Five Ports, and all other Ports, shall have all their Liberties and Free Customs.

[Ch. XI]. Common Pleas shall not follow our Court, but shall be holden in some place certain.

[Ch. XXIX]. No Freeman shall be taken or imprisoned, or disseised of his Freehold, or Liberties, or Free Customs, or be outlawed, or exiled, or any otherwise destroyed, nor will we pass upon him, nor condemn him, but by lawful Judgment of his Peers, or by the Law of the Land. We will sell to no man, we will not deny or defer to any man, either Justice or Right.

A climate of freedom is most conducive to the growth of a healthy society.

JONATHAN BARTRAM, 1792–1854

From Utopia

Sir Thomas More
Author and Lord Chancellor of England
(1478–1535)

This is one of the ancientest laws among them, that no man shall be blamed for reasoning in the maintenance of his own religion. For King Utopus . . . first of all made a decree that it should be lawful for every man to favor and follow what religion he would, and that he might do the best he could to bring others to his opinion, so that he did it peaceably, gently, quietly, and soberly, without haste and contentious rebuking and inveighing against others. And this surely he thought a very unmeet and foolish thing, and a point of arrogant presumption, to compel all others by violence and threatenings to agree to the same thou believest to be true.

Let me warn you this: the king who values his throne, nay, his very life, will grant his subjects the utmost freedom within reason, for there is no man so dangerous as he whos rights have been taken from him, whos will has been subjugated, and whos life has been altered to suit him who calls himself "master." It is not in the nature of man to live but as himself, and the sovereign who seeks to take from him this essential of natural being will find one day that he has created not a willing slave but a monster of vengeance.

AUTHOR UNKNOWN. FRANCE, SEVENTEENTH CENTURY.

DE LAUDIBUS LEGUM ANGLIAE
(In Praise of English Law)
Fortescue, First Chief Justice of England, and later Chancellor to Henry VI

❦

"The King of England can not alter nor change the Laws of his Realm at his pleasure: for why, he governeth his people by power not only royal but also politic. . . . For he can neither change laws without the consent of his subjects nor yet charge them with impositions against their wills: Wherefore his people do frankly and freely enjoy and occupy their own goods, being ruled by such laws as they themselves desire."

You will observe that from Magna Charta to the Declaration of Right, it has been the uniform policy of our constitution to claim and assert our liberties, as an entailed inheritance derived to us from our forefathers, and to be transmitted to our posterity . . . without any reference whatever to any other more general or prior right.

EDMUND BURKE, BRITISH STATESMAN AND ORATOR, 1729–1797

INSCRIPTION ON PLYMOUTH ROCK MONUMENT

This monument marks the first burying ground in Plymouth of the passengers of the Mayflower.

Here, under cover of darkness, the fast-dwindling company laid their dead, leveling the earth above them lest the Indians should know how many were the graves. Reader! History records no nobler venture for faith and freedom than of this Pilgrim band. In weariness and painfulness, in watching, often in hunger and cold, they laid the foundations of a state wherein every man, through countless ages, should have liberty to worship God in his own way. May their example inspire thee to do thy part in perpetuating and spreading the lofty ideals of our republic throughout the world!

Resolved, that the Constitution of Government in this Province is founded on the Rights of Mankind, and the noble Principles of English Liberty, and is therefore perfectly true.

JOHN DICKINSON's draft of the Pennsylvania Assembly Action on the Stamp Act of 1765

PREAMBLE TO THE CONSTITUTION
OF THE UNITED STATES

We, the People of the United States, in order to form a more perfect union, establish justice, insure domestic tranquility, provide for the common defense, promote the general welfare, and secure the blessings of liberty to ourselves and our posterity, do ordain and establish this Constitution for the United States of America.

I have never been able to conceive how any rational being could propose happiness to himself from the exercise of power over others.

THOMAS JEFFERSON

It is the old practice of despots to use a part of the people to keep the rest in order.

THOMAS JEFFERSON

FREEDOM OF THOUGHT
Samuel Adams

Driven from every other corner of the earth, freedom of thought and the right of private judgment in matters of conscience direct their course to this happy country as their last asylum.

The government of a state is much like the office of a guardian or trustee, which should always be managed for the good of the pupil, and not of the persons to whom he is intrusted; and those men who, whilst they take care of one, neglect or disregard another part of the citizens do but occasion sedition and discord, the most destructive things in the world to a state.

CICERO, ROMAN LAWYER, CONSUL, AND SENATOR, 106–43 B.C.

Liberty, after she has been chained up awhile, is always more fierce, and sets her teeth in deeper than she could otherwise have done if she had never been restrained.

CICERO, ROMAN LAWYER, CONSUL, AND SENATOR, 106–43 B.C.

GO DOWN, MOSES
Negro Spiritual

When Israel was in Egypt's land,
    Let my people go;
Oppressed so hard they could not stand,
    Let my people go.

  Go down, Moses,
    Way down in Egypt land,
  Tell ole Pha-roh,
    Let my people go.

Thus saith the Lord, bold Moses said,
    Let my people go;
If not I'll smite your firstborn dead,
    Let my people go.

No more shall they in bondage toil,
    Let my people go;
Let them come out with Egypt's spoil,
    Let my people go.

BOSTON HYMN

Read in Boston Music Hall, January 1, 1863

Ralph Waldo Emerson (1803–1882)

The word of the Lord by night
To the watching Pilgrims came,
As they sat by the seaside,
And filled their hearts with flame.

God said, I am tired of kings,
I suffer them no more;
Up to my ear the morning brings
The outrage of the poor.

Think ye I made this ball
A field of havoc and war,
Where tyrants great and tyrants small
Might harry the weak and poor?

My angel, his name is Freedom—
Choose him to be your king;
He shall cut pathways east and west,
And fend you with his wing.

Lo! I uncover the land
Which I hid of old time in the West,
As the sculptor uncovers the statue
When he has wrought his best;

[42]

I show Columbia, of the rocks
Which dip their foot in the seas,
And soar to the airborne flocks
Of clouds, and the boreal fleece.

I will divide my goods;
Call in the wretch and slave:
None shall rule but the humble,
And none but toil shall have.

I will have never a noble,
No lineage counted great;
Fishers and choppers and ploughmen
Shall constitute a state.

Go, cut down trees in the forest,
And trim the straightest boughs;
Cut down the trees in the forest,
And build me a wooden house.

Call the people together,
The young men and the sires,
The digger in the harvest field,
Hireling, and him that hires;

And here in a pine statehouse
They shall choose men to rule
In every needful faculty,
In church, and state, and school.

Lo, now! if these poor men
Can govern the land and sea,

And make just laws below the sun,
As planets faithful be.

And ye shall succor men;
'Tis nobleness to serve;
Help them who cannot help again:
Beware from right to swerve.

I break your bonds and masterships,
And I unchain the slave:
Free be his heart and hand henceforth
As wind and wandering wave.

I cause from every creature
His proper good to flow:
As much as he is and doeth,
So much he shall bestow.

But laying hands on another
To coin his labor and sweat,
He goes in pawn to his victim
For eternal years in debt.

Today unbind the captive
So only are ye unbound;
Lift up a people from the dust,
Trump of their rescue, sound!

Pay ransom to the owner,
And fill the bag to the brim.
Who is the owner? The slave is owner,
And ever was. Pay him.

[44]

Oh North! give him beauty for rags,
And honor, O South! for his shame;
Nevada! coin thy golden crags
With Freedom's image and name.

Up! And the dusky race
That sat in darkness long—
Be swift their feet as antelopes,
And as behemoth strong.

Come, East and West and North,
By races, as snowflakes,
And carry my purpose forth,
Which neither halts nor shakes.

My will fulfilled shall be,
For, in daylight or in dark,
My thunderbolt has eyes to see
His way home to the mark.

ON FREEDOM
James Russell Lowell

They are slaves who fear to speak
For the fallen and the weak;
They are slaves who will not choose
Hatred, scoffing, and abuse,
Rather than in silence shrink
From the truth they needs must think;
They are slaves who dare not be
In the right with two or three.

There is nothing that more characterizes a complete citizen than having a share in the judicial and executive part of the government.

The most pure democracy is that which is so called principally from that equality which prevails in it; for this is what the law in that state directs: that the poor shall be in no greater subjection than the rich; nor that the supreme power shall be lodged with either of these, but that both shall share it.

ARISTOTLE, GREEK PHILOSOPHER, 384–322 B.C.

LIBERTY AND UNION

from *The Reply to Hayne* (1830)

Daniel Webster

While the Union lasts, we have high, exciting, gratifying prospects spread before us, for us and our children. Beyond that, I seek not to penetrate the veil. God grant that, in my day, at least, that curtain may not rise! God grant that on my vision never may be opened what lies behind! When my eyes shall be turned to behold for the last time the sun in heaven, may I not see him shining on the broken and dishonored fragments of a once-glorious Union; on the States dissevered, discordant, belligerent; on a land rent with civil feuds, or drenched, it may be, in fraternal blood! Let their last feeble and lingering glance rather behold the gorgeous ensign of the Republic, now known and honored throughout the earth, still full high advanced, its arms and trophies streaming in their original luster, not a stripe erased or polluted, nor a single star obscured, bearing for its motto no such miserable interrogatory as, "What is all this worth?" nor those other words of delusion and folly, "Liberty first and Union afterward"; but everywhere, spread all over in characters of living light, blazing on all its ample folds, as they float over the sea and over the land, and in every wind under the whole heavens, that other sentiment dear to every American heart—Liberty *and* Union, now and forever, one and inseparable!

A HOUSE DIVIDED

from *The Lincoln—Douglas debates in Illinois*

Abraham Lincoln

🔔

In his final words tonight the Judge said that we may be "the terror of the world." I don't think we want to be that. I think we would prefer to be the encouragement of the world, the proof that man is at last worthy to be free. But—we shall provide no such encouragement unless we can establish our ability as a nation to live and grow. And we shall surely do neither if these states fail to remain *united*. There can be no distinction in the definitions of liberty, as between one section and another, one race and another, one class and another. "A house divided against itself cannot stand." This government cannot endure permanently half *slave* and half *free!*

Our reliance is in the love of liberty which God has planted in us. Our defense is in the spirit which prizes liberty as the heritage of all men, in all lands everywhere.

ABRAHAM LINCOLN

THE ETERNAL STRUGGLE

from *The Lincoln-Douglas Debates* (1858)

Abraham Lincoln

. . . It is the eternal struggle between these two principles—right and wrong—throughout the world. They are the two principles that have stood face to face from the beginning of time and will ever continue to struggle. The one is the common right of humanity, and the other the divine right of kings. It is the same principle in whatever shape it develops itself. It is the same spirit that says, "You toil and work and earn bread, and I will eat it." No matter in what shape it comes, whether from the mouth of a king who seeks to bestride the people of his own nation and live from the fruit of their labor, or from one race of men as an apology for enslaving another race, it is the same tyrannical principle.

As I would not be a slave, so I would not be a master. This expresses my idea of democracy. Whatever differs from this, to the extent of the difference, is no democracy.

ABRAHAM LINCOLN

[49]

THE SLAVE
James Oppenheim (1882–1932)

They set the slave free, striking off his chains—
Then he was as much of a slave as ever.
He was still chained to servility,
He was still manacled to indolence and sloth,
He was still bound by fear and superstition,
By ignorance, suspicion, and savagery—
His slavery was not in the chains, but in himself—
They can only set free men free
And there is no need of that.
Free men set themselves free.

The spirit of liberty is the spirit of Him who, near two thousand years ago, taught mankind that lesson it has never learned, but has never quite forgotten; that there may be a kingdom where the least shall be heard and considered side by side with the greatest.

JUDGE LEARNED HAND

Benevolence or Justice? I don't care how benevolent the master is going to be, I will not live under a master.

WOODROW WILSON

THE FOUR FREEDOMS
Franklin Delano Roosevelt

In the future days, which we seek to make secure, we look forward to a world founded upon four essential freedoms.

The first is freedom of speech and expression—everywhere in the world.

The second is freedom of every person to worship God in his own way—everywhere in the world.

The third is freedom from want—which, translated into world terms, means economic understandings which will secure to every nation a healthy peaceful life for its inhabitants—everywhere in the world.

The fourth is freedom from fear—which, translated into world terms, means a worldwide reduction of armaments to such a point and in such a thorough fashion that no nation will be in a position to commit an act of aggression against any neighbor—anywhere in the world.

No one can make you feel inferior without your consent.
ELEANOR ROOSEVELT

The rare individual who has learned to govern himself is too fed up with the labor of it to want to govern anybody else.
HENRY S. HASKINS

Amongst the many changes and alterations which Lycurgus made, the first and of greatest importance was the establishment of the Senate, which, having a power equal to the king's in matters of great consequence, did (as Plato expresses it) with its phlegm allay and qualify the hot complexion of a monarchy, served as a rampart against the insolence of the people, and always kept the commonwealth in good temper. For the state which before had no firm basis to stand upon, but leaned one while toward an absolute monarchy (when the kings had the upper hand) and another while toward a pure democracy (when the people had the better of it) found in this establishment of the Senate a counterpoise, which always kept things in a just equilibrium. For the twenty-eight always adhered to the weaker side, and put themselves like a weight into the lighter scale, until they had reduced the other to a balance.

PLUTARCH, GREEK PHILOSOPHER AND BIOGRAPHER 46?–120? A.D.

We are happy in a form of government which cannot envy the laws of our neighbors; for it hath served as a model to others, but is original at Athens. And this our form, as committed not to the *few*, but to the whole body of the people, is called a *democracy*.

THUCYDIDES, GREEK HISTORIAN, 431 B.C.

III

THE PEOPLE SING

I HEAR AMERICA SINGING
Walt Whitman (1819–1892)

I hear America singing, the varied carols I hear:
Those of mechanics—each one singing his, as it should be, blithe
    and strong;
The carpenter singing his, as he measures his plank or beam,
The mason singing his, as he makes ready for work, or leaves off
    work;
The boatman singing what belongs to him in his boat—the deck-
    hand singing on the steamboat deck;
The shoemaker singing as he sits on his bench—the hatter singing
    as he stands;
The woodcutter's song—the plowboy's on his way in the morning,
    or at noon intermission, or at sundown;
The delicious singing of the mother—or of the young wife at
    work—or of the girl sewing or washing—
Each singing what belongs to him or her and to none else;
The day what belongs to the day—at night, the party of young
    fellows, robust, friendly,
Singing, with open mouths, their strong melodious songs.

YANKEE DOODLE
Edward Bangs

Father and I went down to camp,
  Along with Captain Gooding,
And there we see the men and boys,
  As thick as hasty pudding.

Chorus:
Yankee Doodle, keep it up,
  Yankee Doodle, dandy,
Mind the music and the step,
  And with the girls be handy.

And there we see a thousand men,
  As rich as Squire David;
And what they wasted every day
  I wish it could be savèd.

The 'lasses they eat every day
  Would keep our house a winter;
They have so much that, I'll be bound,
  They eat whene'er they're a mind to.

And there we see a swamping gun,
  As big as a log of maple,
Upon a deucèd little cart,
  A load for father's cattle.

And every time they shoot it off,

[55]

It takes a horn of powder,
And makes a noise like father's gun,
Only a nation louder.

I went as nigh to one myself
As Siah's underpinning;
And father went as nigh again,
I thought the deuce was in him.

Cousin Simon grew so bold,
I though he would have cocked it,
It scared me so I shrinked it off,
And hung by father's pocket.

And Captain Davis had a gun,
He kind of clapped his hand on't,
And stuck a crooked stabbing-iron
Upon the little end on't.

And there I see a pumpkin shell
As big as mother's basin;
And every time they touched it off,
They scampered like the nation.

I see a little barrel, too,
The heads were made of leather,
They knocked upon't with little clubs
To call the folks together.

And there was Captain Washington,
And gentlefolks about him,
They say he's grown so tarnal proud
He will not ride without 'em.

He had got on his meeting clothes,
  And rode a strapping stallion,
And gave his orders to the men—
  I guess there was a million.

The flaming ribbons in his hat,
  They looked so tearing fine ah,
I wanted peskily to get,
  To give to my Jemima.

And then I see a snarl of men
  A digging graves, they told me.
So tarnal long, so tarnal deep,
  They 'tended they should hold me.

It scared me so, I hooked it off,
  Nor stopped, as I remember,
Nor turned about, till I got home,
  Locked up in mother's chamber.

AMERICA THE BEAUTIFUL
Katharine Lee Bates (1859–1929)

O beautiful for spacious skies,
For amber waves of grain,
For purple mountain majesties
Above the fruited plain!
America! America!
God shed His grace on thee
And crown thy good with brotherhood
From sea to shining sea!

O beautiful for pilgrim feet,
Whose stern, impassioned stress
A thoroughfare for freedom beat
Across the wilderness!
America! America!
God mend thine every flaw,
Confirm thy soul in self-control,
Thy liberty in law!

O beautiful for heroes proved
In liberating strife,
Who more than self their country loved,
And mercy more than life!
America! America!
May God thy gold refine
Till all success be nobleness
And every gain divine!

THE BATTLE-CRY OF FREEDOM
George F. Root (1820–1895)

The Union forever, hurrah, boys, hurrah!
Down with the traitor and up with the star;
While we rally round the flag, boys, rally once again,
Shouting the battle-cry of Freedom.

We are springing to the call of our brothers gone before,
Shouting the battle-cry of Freedom;
And we'll fill the vacant ranks with a million freemen more,
Shouting the battle-cry of Freedom.

We will welcome to our numbers the loyal, true, and brave,
Shouting the battle-cry of Freedom;
And altho' they may be poor, not a man shall be a slave,
Shouting the battle-cry of Freedom;
And we'll hurl the rebel crew from the land we love the best.
Shouting the battle-cry of Freedom.

COLUMBIA, THE GEM OF THE OCEAN

First sung in Philadelphia about 1843

Author Unknown

O Columbia, the gem of the ocean,
   The home of the brave and the free,
The shrine of each patriot's devotion,
   A world offers homage to thee.
Thy mandates make heroes assemble
   When Liberty's form stands in view;
Thy banners make tyranny tremble
   When borne by the red, white and blue.
     When borne by the red, white and blue,
     When borne by the red, white and blue,
     Thy banners make tyranny tremble
     When borne by the red, white and blue.

When war winged its wide desolation
   And threatened the land to deform,
The ark then of freedom's foundation,
   Columbia, rode safe thro' the storm:
With the garlands of vict'ry around her,
   When so proudly she bore her brave crew,
With her flag proudly floating before her,
   The boast of the red, white and blue.
The boast of the red, white and blue,
The boast of the red, white and blue,
With her flag proudly floating before her,
The boast of the red, white and blue.

The star-spangled banner bring hither,
　O'er Columbia's true sons let it wave;
May the wreaths they have won never wither,
　Nor its stars cease to shine on the brave:
May the service, united, ne'er sever,
　But hold to their colors so true;
The army and navy forever,
　Three cheers for the red, white and blue.
　　Three cheers for the red, white and blue,
　　Three cheers for the red, white and blue,
　　The army and navy forever,
　　Three cheers for the red, white and blue

AMERICA
Samuel Francis Smith (1808–1895)

My country, 'tis of thee,
Sweet land of liberty,
  Of thee I sing;
Land where my fathers died,
Land of the Pilgrims' pride,
From every mountain-side
  Let Freedom ring.

My native country, thee,
Land of the noble free—
  Thy name I love;
I love thy rocks and rills,
Thy woods and templed hills:
My heart with rapture thrills
  Like that above.

Let music swell the breeze,
And ring from all the trees
  Sweet Freedoms's song;
Let mortal tongues awake,
Let all that breathe partake,
Let rocks their silence break—
  The sound prolong.

Our fathers' God, to Thee,
Author of liberty,

To Thee we sing;
Long may our land be bright
With Freedom's holy light;
Protect us by Thy might,
Great God, our King.

THE STAR-SPANGLED BANNER

Written during the bombardment of Fort McHenry,
September 3, 1814

Francis Scott Key (1779–1843)

O say, can you see, by the dawn's early light,
What so proudly we hailed at the twilight's last gleaming.
Whose broad stripes and bright stars, through the perilous fight,
O'er the ramparts we watched were so gallantly streaming!
And the rockets' red glare, the bombs bursting in air,
Gave proof through the night that our flag was still there:
O say, does that star-spangled banner yet wave
O'er the land of the free and the home of the brave?

On the shore, dimly seen through the mists of the deep,
Where the foe's haughty host in dread silence reposes,
What is that which the breeze, o'er the towering steep,
As it fitfully blows, half conceals, half discloses?
Now it catches the gleam of the morning's first beam,
In full glory reflected now shines on the stream.
'Tis the star-spangled banner! O long may it wave
O'er the land of the free and the home of the brave!

And where is that band who so vauntingly swore
That the havoc of war and the battle's confusion
A home and a country should leave us no more?
Their blood has washed out their foul footsteps' pollution.
No refuge could save the hireling and slave
From the terror of flight, or the gloom of the grave:

And the star-spangled banner in triumph doth wave
O'er the land of the free and the home of the brave!

O thus be it ever, when freemen shall stand
Between their loved homes and the war's desolation!
Blest with victory and peace, may the heaven-rescued land
Praise the Power that hath made and preserved us a nation.
Then conquer we must, when our cause it is just,
And this be our motto: "In God is our trust,"
And the star-spangled banner in triumph shall wave
O'er the land of the free and the home of the brave!

THE FLAG GOES BY
Henry Holcomb Bennett (1863–1924)

Hats off!
Along the street there comes
A blare of bugles, a ruffle of drums,
A flash of color beneath the sky:
Hats off!
The flag is passing by!

Blue and crimson and white it shines,
Over the steel-tipped, ordered lines.
Hats off!
The colors before us fly;
But more than the flag is passing by:

Sea-fights and land-fights, grim and great,
Fought to make and to save the State;
Weary marches and sinking ships;
Cheers of victory on dying lips;

Days of plenty and years of peace;
March of a strong land's swift increase;
Equal justice, right and law,
Stately honor and reverend awe;

Sign of a nation, great and strong
To ward her people from foreign wrong:
Pride and glory and honor—all
Live in the colors to stand or fall.

Hats off!
Along the street there comes
A blare of bugles, a ruffle of drums;
And loyal hearts are beating high:
Hats off!
The flag is passing by!

THE BATTLE HYMN OF THE REPUBLIC
Julia Ward Howe (1819–1910)

Mine eyes have seen the glory of the coming of the Lord;
He is trampling out the vintage where the grapes of wrath are
    stored;
He has loosed the fateful lightning of His terrible swift sword;
  His truth is marching on.

I have seen Him in the watch fires of a hundred circling camps;
They have builded Him an altar in the evening dews and damps;
I have read His righteous sentence in the dim and flaring lamps;
  His day is marching on.

I have read a fiery gospel, writ in burnished rows of steel;
"As ye deal with my contemners, so with you my grace shall deal";
Let the hero, born of woman, crush the serpent with his heel,
  Since God is marching on.

He has sounded forth the trumpet that shall never call retreat;
He is sifting out the hearts of men before His judgment seat;
Oh, be swift, my soul, to answer Him! be jubilant, my feet!
  Our God is marching on.

In the beauty of the lilies Christ was born across the sea,
With a glory in His bosom that transfigures you and me;
As He died to make men holy, let us die to make men free,
  While God is marching on.

Chorus:
Glory, glory hallelujah! Glory, glory hallelujah!
Glory, glory hallelujah! His truth is marching on.

LAND OF HOPE AND GLORY

Arthur C. Benson
English writer (1862–1925)

Dear Land of Hope, thy hope is crowned,
God make thee mightier yet!
On sovereign brows, beloved renowned,
Once more thy crown is set,
Thine equal laws, by Freedom gained,
Have ruled thee well and long;
By Freedom gained, by Truth maintained,
Thine Empire shall be strong.

Thy fame is ancient as the days,
As Ocean large and wide;
A pride that dares, and heeds not praise,
A stern and silent pride;
Not that false joy that dreams content
With that our sires have won,
The blood a hero sire hath spent
Still nerves a hero son.

Chorus:
Land of Hope and Glory, mother of the Free.
How shall we extol thee, who are born of thee?
Wider still and wider shall thy bounds be set;
God who made thee mighty, make thee mightier yet.

BRUCE TO HIS MEN AT BANNOCKBURN
Robert Burns
Scottish poet (1759–1790)

Scots, wha hae wi' Wallace bled,
Scots wham Bruce has aften led;
Welcome to your gory bed,
   Or to victory!

Now's the day, and now's the hour:
See the front o' battle lour:
See approach proud Edward's power—
   Chains and slavery!

Wha will be a traitor knave?
Wha can fill a coward's grave?
Wha sae base as be a slave?
   Let him turn and flee!

Wha for Scotland's king and law
Freedom's sword will strongly draw,
Freeman stand, or freeman fa',
   Let him follow me!

By oppression's woes and pains!
By your sons in servile chains,
We will drain our dearest veins,
   But they shall be free!

Lay the proud usurpers low!
Tyrants tall in every foe!
Liberty's in every blow!
  Let us do or die!

THE MARSEILLAISE

Translated by Charles H. Kerr

Rouget De Lisle (1760–1836)

Ye sons of freedom, wake to glory!
Hark! Hark! what myriads bid you rise!
Your children, wives, and grandsires hoary,
Behold their tears and hear their cries!
Shall hateful tyrants, mischief breeding,
With hireling ghosts, a ruffian band,
Affright and desolate the land,
While peace and liberty lie bleeding?
To arms! To arms, ye brave!
The avenging sword unsheathe;
March on! march on! all hearts resolved
On victory or death.

Now, now the dangerous storm is rolling,
Which treacherous kings, confederate, raise;
The dogs of war, let loose, are howling,
And lo! our fields and cities blaze;
And shall we basely view the ruin,
While lawless force, with guilty stride,
Spreads desolation far and wide,
With crimes and blood his hands imbruing?

With luxury and pride surrounded,
The vile, insatiate despots dare,
Their thirst of power and gold unbounded,

To meet and vend the light and air;
Like beasts of burden would they load us,
Like gods would bid their slaves adore;
But man is man and who is more?
Then, shall they longer lash and goad us?

O Liberty! can man resign thee,
Once having felt thy generous flame?
Can dungeons, bolts, or bars confine thee?
Or whips thy noble spirit tame?
Too long the world has wept, bewailing
That falsehood's dagger tyrants wield,
But freedom is our sword and shield,
And all their arts are unavailing.
To arms! to arms, ye brave!
The avenging sword unsheathe;
March on! march on! all hearts resolved
On victory or death.

IV

SING OF THE BRAVE
AND THE MIRACLES
THEY WROUGHT

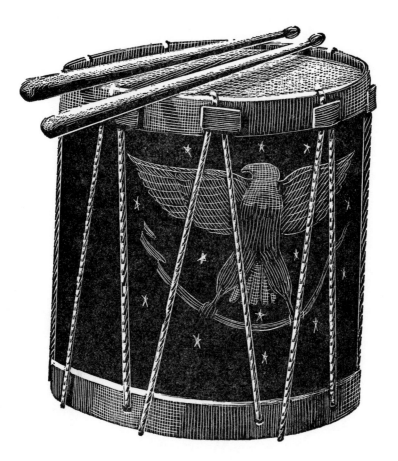

SING OF THE BRAVE
Laurence Altgood

Sing of the brave and the miracles they wrought;
Sing of the battle nobly fought;
Waste no tear on the coward's grave!
Save your heart for the deathless brave.

HEROISM
Ralph Waldo Emerson (1803–1882)

Times of heroism are generally times of terror, but the day never shines in which this element may not work. The circumstances of man, we say, are historically somewhat better in this country and at this hour than perhaps ever before. More freedom exists for culture. It will not now run against an ax at the first step out of the beaten track of opinion. But whoso is heroic will always find crises to try his edge. Human virtue demands her champions and martyrs, and the trial of persecution always proceeds. It is but the other day that the brave Lovejoy gave his breast to the bullets of a mob, for the rights of free speech and opinion, and died when it was better not to live.

WHERE ARE YOU GOING, GREAT-HEART?
John Oxenham

Where are you going, Great-Heart,
With your eager face and your fiery grace?
　Where are you going, Great-Heart?

"To fight a fight with all my might;
For Truth and Justice, God and Right;
To grace all Life and His fair Light."
　Then God go with you, Great-Heart!

Where are you going, Great-Heart?
"To live Today above the Past;
To make Tomorrow sure and fast;
To nail God's colors to the mast."
　Then God go with you, Great-Heart!

Where are you going, Great-Heart?
"To break down old dividing lines;
To carry out my Lord's designs;
To build again His broken shrines."
　Then God go with you, Great-Heart!

Where are you going, Great-Heart?
"To set all burdened peoples free;
To win for all God's liberty;
To 'stablish His Sweet Sovereignty."
　God goeth with you, Great-Heart!

GREAT MEN

from *"Charles Sumner"*

Henry Wadsworth Longfellow (1807–1882)

When a great man dies,
For years beyond our ken
The light he leaves behind him lies
Upon the paths of men.

[79]

HOW SLEEP THE BRAVE

William Collins
English poet (1721–1759)

How sleep the brave, who sink to rest
By all their country's wishes blest!
When Spring, with dewy fingers cold,
Returns to deck their hallowed mold,
She there shall dress a sweeter sod
Than Fancy's feet have ever trod.

By fairy hands their knell is rung;
By forms unseen their dirge is sung;
There Honor comes, a pilgrim gray,
To bless the turf that wraps their clay;
And Freedom shall awhile repair
To dwell, a weeping hermit, there!

THE CHARGE OF THE LIGHT BRIGADE
AT BALACLAVA
Alfred, Lord Tennyson
English poet (1809–1892)

Half a league, half a league,
  Half a league onward,
All in the valley of Death
  Rode the six hundred.
"Forward the Light Brigade!
Charge for the guns!" he said:
Into the valley of Death
  Rode the six hundred.

"Forward the Light Brigade!"
Was there a man dismayed?
Not though the soldier knew
  Someone had blundered:
Theirs not to make reply,
Theirs not to reason why,
Theirs but to do and die:
Into the valley of Death
  Rode the six hundred.

Cannon to right of them,
Cannon to left of them,
Cannon in front of them
  Volleyed and thundered.
Stormed at with shot and shell,

Boldly they rode and well,
Into the jaws of Death,
Into the mouth of Hell
    Rode the six hundred.

Flashed all their sabres bare,
Flashed as they turned in air
Sabring the gunners there,
Charging an army, while
    All the world wondered.
Plunged in the battery-smoke
Right through the line they broke;
Cossack and Russian
Reeled from the sabre-stroke,
    Shattered and sundered.
Then they rode back, but not,
    Not the six hundred.

Cannon to right of them,
Cannon to left of them,
Cannon behind them
    Volleyed and thundered;
Stormed at with shot and shell,
While horse and hero fell,
They that had fought so well
Came through the jaws of Death,
Back from the mouth of Hell,
All that was left of them,
Left of six hundred.

When can their glory fade?
O the wild charge they made!

All the world wondered.
Honor the charge they made!
Honor the Light Brigade,
  Noble six hundred!

COLUMBUS
Joaquin Miller (1839–1913)

🔔

Behind him lay the gray Azores,
  Behind the Gates of Hercules;
Before him not the ghost of shores,
  Before him only shoreless seas.
The good mate said: "Now must we pray
  For lo! the very stars are gone.
Brave Admiral, speak, what shall I say?"
  "Why, say 'Sail on! sail on! and on!' "

"My men grow mutinous day by day;
  My men grow ghastly wan and weak."
The stout mate thought of home; a spray
  Of salt wave washed his swarthy cheek.
"What shall I say, brave Admiral, say,
  If we sight naught but seas at dawn?"
"Why, you shall say at break of day,
  'Sail on! sail on! sail on! and on!' "

They sailed and sailed, as winds might blow,
  Until at last the blanched mate said:
"Why, now not even God would know
  Should I and all my men fall dead.
These very winds forget their way,
  For God from these dread seas is gone.
Now speak, brave Admiral, speak and say"—
  He said: "Sail on! sail on! and on!"

They sailed. They sailed. Then spake the mate:
  "This mad sea shows his teeth tonight.
He curls his lip, he lies in wait,
  With lifted teeth, as if to bite!
Brave Admiral, say but one good word:
  What shall we do when hope is gone?"
The words leapt like a leaping sword:
  "Sail on! sail on! sail on! and on!"

Then, pale and worn, he kept his deck,
  And peered through darkness. Ah, that night
Of all dark nights! And then a speck—
  A light! a light! a light! a light!
It grew, a starlit flag unfurled!
  It grew to be Time's burst of dawn.
He gained a world; he gave that world
  Its grandest lesson: "On! sail on!"

ROGER WILLIAMS
James Daugherty

🔔

I.

He came to the wilderness seeking freedom of religion and speech,
And that was all right in Boston in 1631.
So they made quite a fuss over him at first.
He built with his own hands a stout clapboard house for his
    young wife, and started a trading post with the Indians.
He treated them honestly, which was somewhat irregular,
And respected them enough to learn their language.

II.

When he began to preach about freedom of conscience
And every man's having a right to seek the inner light,
He became a nuisance and then a problem with the Boston
    hierarchy.
But as he was an English gentleman, a minister of the gospel,
    and
Had powerful friends in England,
He could not be whipped or have his ears cropped,
As was the usual custom.
So they banished him.
There was no place to go except the wilderness
Or back to Old England.
He could stay in the colony six months longer, they granted,
If he would keep his mouth shut; and he promised.

III.

But at his home in Salem he kept on talking
To neighbors who came to his house.
When the constables from Boston came to arrest him and put
    him aboard ship for England
He was gone.
But not to England.
He was trekking across the forty miles of wilderness through
    the February blizzards
To his old friend Massasoit, the Sagamore of the Wampanoags,
Who was not fussy about fine points in theology;
Only knowing a brave and generous man when he saw one.
He gave food and shelter freely.
When the snow melted, Williams struck out with a handful
    who followed him,
Finding a place to build on the genial shore of Narragansett Bay.
Providence, he called the little settlement.

IV.

He made it a haven for the persecuted, of whom there was then
As now a God's plenty—Quaker, Baptist, Jew, Catholic—
A democracy where each could worship God in his own way,
Having freedom of conscience, as it was called.
You did not have to fit the pattern—decency and good will were
    enough.
Then the scared elders of the Bay sent begging he save their
    scalps from the Indian uprising, for the Pequots were angry,
    planning massacre.
He spent days convincing the angry chiefs at the risk of his life,
    and made peace, saving their scalps, without thanks.
Later the Massachusetts Gideons exterminated the whole Pequot
    tribe in one bloody night's work, roasting women and chil-
    dren in the burning palisade.

V.

He had a tongue like a sword, and he used it so against tyrants
    and persecutors and the accusers of the innocent:
"Having bought truth dear, we must not sell it cheap,
    not the least grain of it for the whole world; no,
    not for the saving of souls, though our own most precious;
    least of all for the bitter sweetening of a little vanishing
    pleasure,
    for a little puff of credit and reputation from the changeable
    breath of uncertain sons of men."

POCAHONTAS

William Makepeace Thackeray,
English poet and novelist (1811–1863)

Wearied arm and broken sword
 Wage in vain the desperate fight;
Round him press a countless horde,
 He is but a single knight.
Hark! a cry of triumph shrill
 Through the wilderness resounds
 As, with twenty bleeding wounds,
Sinks the warrior, fighting still.

Now they heap the funeral pyre,
 And the torch of death they light;
Ah! 'tis hard to die by fire!
 Who shall shield the captive knight
Round the stake with fiendish cry
 Wheel and dance the savage crowd,
 Cold the victim's mien and proud,
And his breast is bared to die.

Who shall shield the fearless heart?
 Who avert the murderous blade?
From the throng with sudden start
 See, there springs an Indian maid.
Quick she stands before the knight:
 "Loose the chain, unbind the ring
 I am daughter of the king,
And I claim the Indian right!

Dauntlessly aside she flings
   Lifted ax and thirsty knife,
Fondly to his heart she clings,
   And her bosom guards his life!
In the woods of Powhatan,
   Still 'tis told by Indian fires,
   How a daughter of their sires
Saved a captive Englishman.

PAUL REVERE'S RIDE
Henry Wadsworth Longfellow (1807–1882)

Listen, my children, and you shall hear
Of the midnight ride of Paul Revere,
On the eighteenth of April, in Seventy-five;
Hardly a man is now alive
Who remembers that famous day and year.

He said to his friend, "If the British march
By land or sea from the town tonight,
Hang a lantern aloft in the belfry arch
Of the North Church tower as a signal light—
One, if by land, and two, if by sea;
And I on the opposite shore will be,
Ready to ride and spread the alarm
Through every Middlesex village and farm,
For the country folk to be up and to arm."

Then he said, "Good night!" and with muffled oar
Silently rowed to the Charlestown shore,
Just as the moon rose over the bay,
Where swinging wide at her moorings lay
The Somerset, British man-of-war;
A phantom ship, with each mast and spar
Across the moon like a prison bar,
And a huge black hulk, that was magnified
By its own reflection in the tide.
Meanwhile, his friend, through alley and street,

Wanders and watches, with eager ears,
Till in the silence around him he hears
The muster of men at the barrack door,
The sound of arms, and the tramp of feet,
And the measured tread of the grenadiers,
Marching down to their boats on the shore.

Then he climbed to the tower of the Old North Church,
By the wooden stairs, with stealthy tread,
To the belfry-chamber overhead,
And startled the pigeons from their perch
On the somber rafters, that round him made
Masses and moving shapes of shade—
By the trembling ladder, steep and tall,
To the highest window in the wall,
Where he paused to listen and look down
A moment on the roofs of the town,
And the moonlight flowing over all.

Beneath in the churchyard, lay the dead,
In their night-encampment on the hill,
Wrapped in silence so deep and still
That he could hear, like a sentinel's tread,
The watchful night-wind, as it went
Creeping along from tent to tent,
And seeming to whisper, "All is well!"
A moment only he feels the spell
Of the place and the hour, and the secret dread
Of the lonely belfry and the dead;
For suddenly all his thoughts are bent
On a shadowy something far away,
Where the river widens to meet the bay—
A line of black that bends and floats

On the rising tide, like a bridge of boats.

Meanwhile, impatient to mount and ride,
Booted and spurred, with a heavy stride
On the opposite shore walked Paul Revere.
Now he patted his horse's side,
Now gazed at the landscape far and near,
Then, impetuous, stamped the earth,
And turned and tightened his saddle girth;
But mostly he watched with eager search
The belfry tower of the Old North Church,
As it rose above the graves on the hill,
Lonely and spectral and somber and still.
And lo! as he looks, on the belfry's height
A glimmer, and then a gleam of light!
He springs to the saddle, the bridle he turns,
But lingers and gazes, till full on his sight
A second lamp in the belfry burns!

A hurry of hoofs in a village street,
A shape in the moonlight, a bulk in the dark,
And beneath, from the pebbles, in passing, a spark
Struck out by a steed flying fearless and fleet:
That was all! And yet, through the gloom and the light,
The fate of a nation was riding that night;
And the spark struck out by that steed, in his flight,
Kindled the land into flame with its heat.

He has left the village and mounted the steep,
And beneath him, tranquil and broad and deep,
Is the Mystic, meeting the ocean tides;
And under the alders that skirt its edge,

Now soft on the sand, now loud on the ledge,
Is heard the tramp of his steed as he rides.

It was twelve by the village clock,
When he crossed the bridge into Medford town.
He heard the crowing of the cock,
And the barking of the farmer's dog,
And felt the damp of the river fog,
That rises after the sun goes down.
It was one by the village clock,
When he galloped into Lexington.
He saw the gilded weathercock
Swim in the moonlight as he passed,
And the meetinghouse windows, blank and bare,
Gaze at him with a spectral glare,
As if they already stood aghast
At the bloody work they would look upon.
It was two by the village clock,
When he came to the bridge in Concord town.
He heard the bleating of the flock,
And the twitter of birds among the trees,
And felt the breath of the morning breeze
Blowing over the meadows brown.
And one was safe and asleep in his bed
Who at the bridge would be first to fall,
Who that day would be lying dead,
Pierced by a British musket-ball.

You know the rest. In the books you have read
How the British Regulars fired and fled—
How the farmers gave them ball for ball,
From behind each fence and farmyard wall,

Chasing the redcoats down the lane,
Then crossing the fields to emerge again
Under the trees at the turn of the road,
And only pausing to fire and load.

So through the night rode Paul Revere;
And so through the night went his cry of alarm
To every Middlesex village and farm—
A cry of defiance and not of fear,
A voice in the darkness, a knock at the door,
And a word that shall echo forevermore!
For, borne on the night-wind of the Past,
Through all our history, to the last,
In the hour of darkness and peril and need,
The people will awaken and listen to hear
The hurrying hoofbeats of the steed,
And the midnight message of Paul Revere.

THE NAME OF WASHINGTON
Arthur Gordon Field

America, the land beloved,
    Today reveres the name of him
Whose character was free from guile,
    Whose fame the ages cannot dim.

They called him proud, but erred therein;
    No lord was he, though high of birth;
Though sprung from England's lofty peers,
    He served the lowliest of earth.

He turned his back on pride of name,
    On motherland and luxury,
To weld a horde of quarreling men
    Into a nation proudly free.

Wherever liberty is found,
    Wherever shines fair freedom's sun,
Men count America a friend
    And bless the name of Washington.

OURS, AND ALL MEN'S

from *Under the Old Elm*

James Russell Lowell

Soldier and statesman, rarest unison,
High-poised example of great duties done
Simply as breathing, a world's honors worn
As life's indifferent gifts to all men born;
Dumb for himself, unless it were to God,
But for his barefoot soldier eloquent,
Tramping the snow to coral where they trod,
Held by his awe in hollow-eyed content;
Modest, yet firm as Nature's self; unblamed
Save by the men his nobler temper shamed;
Not honored then or now because he wooed
The popular voice, but that he still withstood;
Broadminded, higher-souled, there is but one
Who was all this and ours, and all men's—WASHINGTON.

AT MOUNT VERNON
Thomas Curtis Clark

Along this path he walked, great Washington,
Who built a nation out of selfish men;
These trees he planted, here he stood and mused
On spring's first blossoms, or on autumn's gain.
By this loved river, flowing wide and free,
He sighed for rest from all the cares of state.
How dear his home! And yet he could not pause
While traitors tore his land with greed and hate;
He could not free himself, whose character
Was part and parcel of his country's name.
He found no lasting rest, though worn and spent,
Till death relieved him from the bonds of fame.
Through all the years, till freedom's day is run,
One name shall shine with splendor—WASHINGTON.

TO WASHINGTON

(Act One, Scene Two, of *Valley Forge*)

Maxwell Anderson

Lift your eyes, my men, and greet the sunrise,
  Soldiers, the dawn of liberty is ours
Long we've battled, long we've faced the foeman
  To gain at least six feet of earth—and flowers.

Twixt liberty and death we pause no longer,
  No choice remains to disconcert the brave;
Races are to the swift, power to the stronger—
  Taxes we will not pay; we choose—the grave.

I am that Washington on whom you've pondered;
  My head is in the clouds, my feet—in mud.
My socks are wet, my shirts are never laundered,
  I grind the neighbors' children up for food.

NATHAN HALE
Francis Miles Finch (1827–1907)

To drumbeat, and heartbeat,
  A soldier marches by;
There is color in his cheek,
  There is courage in his eye,
Yet to drumbeat and heartbeat
  In a moment he must die.

By the starlight and moonlight,
  He seeks the Briton's camp;
He hears the rustling flag,
  And the armed sentry's tramp;
And the starlight and moonlight
  His silent wanderings lamp.

With slow tread and still tread,
  He scans the tented line;
And he counts the battery guns,
  By the gaunt and shadowy pine;
And his slow tread and still tread
  Gives no warning sign.

The dark wave, the plumed wave,
  It meets his eager glance;
And it sparkles 'neath the stars,
  Like the glimmer of a lance—

A dark wave, a plumed wave,
  On an emerald expanse.

A sharp clang, a steel clang,
  And terror in the sound!
For the sentry, falcon-eyed,
  In the camp a spy hath found;
With a sharp clang, a steel clang,
  The patriot is bound.

With calm brow, and steady brow,
  He listens to his doom;
In his look there is no fear,
  Nor a shadow-trace of gloom;
But with calm brow and steady brow,
  He robes him for the tomb.

In the long night, the still night,
  He kneels upon the sod;
And the brutal guards withhold
  E'en the solemn Word of God!
In the long night, the still night,
  He walks where Christ hath trod.

'Neath the blue morn, the sunny morn,
  He dies upon the tree;
And he mourns that he can lose
  But one life for Liberty;
And in the blue morn, the sunny morn,
  His spirit wings are free.

But his last words, his message-words,
    They burn, lest friendly eye
Should read how proud and calm
    A patriot could die,
With his last words, his dying words,
    A soldier's battle cry.

From the Fame-leaf and Angel-leaf
    From monument and urn,
The sad of earth, the glad of heaven,
    His tragic fate shall learn;
But on Fame-leaf and Angel-leaf
    The name of HALE shall burn!

WARREN'S ADDRESS AT BUNKER HILL

June 16, 1775

John Pierpont (1785–1866)

Stand! the ground's your own, my braves!
Will ye give it up to slaves?
Will ye look for greener graves?
   Hope ye mercy still?
What's the mercy despots feel?
Hear it in that battle-peal!
Read it on yon bristling steel!
   Ask it—ye who will.

Fear ye foes who kill for hire?
Will ye to your homes retire?
Look behind you!—they're afire!
   And, before you, see
Who have done it! From the vale
On they come—and will ye quail?
Leaden rain and iron hail
   Let their welcome be!

In the God of battles trust!
Die we may—and die we must:
But, O, where can dust to dust
   Be consigned so well,
As where heaven its dews shall shed
On the martyred patriot's bed,
And the rocks shall raise their head,
   Of his deeds to tell?

[103]

VALLEY FORGE
Maxwell Anderson

Lafayette to Washington:
    Shall I begin by saying
some things you know, but may have forgotten? This world
you have cut from the wilderness, is a new world, brighter
with sun in summer, colder with winter cold
than the world I knew. The air's strange-sharp, the voice
rings here with a hard ring. I find no man
but looks you in the eye and says his thought
in your teeth, and means it. This was not known before
on this star we inhabit. Europe has thirty kings
and a hundred million slaves. But here in this land
each man is a king and walks like a king, each woman
bears herself regally, like a queen. You will find
this is not easy to throw away. The air
of this coast has fired your blood and while three among you,
no more than three, hold hard against the old masters,
the kingdoms lessen and dwindle. They've felt your breath
and feared it, in the old world. Lose! now the gods
in heaven hear me, you cannot lose! Bow down
and humble yourselves if you can! It's not in you to bow
nor to speak humbly. It's a trick you've never learned
and cannot learn in this air!—As for these thrones
that men have bowed to, I've come from them lately and seen
    them,
how they're eaten down with old vices and slimed with worms
'til they crumble into moats! Lower your muzzles,
droop your flags! Even so the kingdoms falter
and go down of themselves!

BETTY ZANE—SEPTEMBER, 1777
Thomas Dunn English (1819–1902)

A century since, out in the West,
A blockhouse was by Girty pressed—
Girty, the renegade, the dread
Of all that border, fiercely led
Five hundred Wyandots to gain
Plunder and scalp-locks from the slain;
And in this hold—Fort Henry then,
But Wheeling now—twelve boys and men
Guarded with watchful ward and care
Women and prattling children there,
Against their rude and savage foes,
And Betty Zane was one of those.

. . .

Now Betty's brothers and her sire
Were with her in this ring of fire,
And she was ready in her way,
To aid their labor day by day,
In all a quiet maiden might.
To mold the bullets for the fight,
And, quick to note and so report,
Watch every act outside the fort;
Or, peering through the loopholes, see
Each phase of savage strategy—
These were her tasks, and thus the maid
The toil-worn garrison could aid.

[105]

Still drearily the fight went on
Until a week had nearly gone,
When it was told—a whisper first,
And then in loud alarm it burst—
Their powder scarce was growing; they
Knew where a keg unopened lay
Outside the fort at Zane's—what now?
Their leader stood with anxious brow.
It must be had at any cost,
Or toil and fort and lives were lost.
Someone must do that work of fear;
What man of men would volunteer?

Two offered and so earnest they,
Neither his purpose would give way;
And Shepherd, who commanded, dare
Not pick or choose between the pair.
But ere they settled on the one
By whom the errand should be done,
Young Betty interposed and said,
"Let me essay the task instead.
Small matter 'twere if Betty Zane,
A useless woman should be slain;
But death, if death of one of those,
Gives too much vantage to our foes."

Her father smiled with pleasure grim—
Her pluck gave painful pride to him;
And while her brothers clamored "No"
He uttered "Boys, let Betty go!
She'll do it at less risk than you;
But keep her steady in your view,

And be your rifles shields for her.
If yonder foe make step or stir,
Pick off each wretch who draws a bead,
And so you'd serve her in her need.
Now I recover from surprise,
I think our Betty's purpose wise."

The gate was opened, on she sped;
The foe astonished, gazed, 'tis said,
And wondered at her purpose, till
She gained that log hut by the hill.
But when in apron wrapped the cask
She backward bore to close her task,
The foemen saw her aim at last
And poured their fire upon her fast.
Bullet on bullet near her fell,
While rang the Indians' angry yell;
But safely through that whirring rain,
Powder in arms, came Betty Zane.

. . .

A hundred years have passed since then;
The savage never came again.
Girty is dust; alike are dead
Those who assailed and those bestead.
Upon those half-cleared, rolling lands,
A crowded city proudly stands;
But of the many who reside
By green Ohio's rushing tide,
Not one has lineage prouder than
(Be he poor or rich) the man
Who boasts that in his spotless strain
Mingles the blood of Betty Zane.

MOLLY PITCHER
Kate Brownlee Sherwood

It was hurry and scurry at Monmouth town,
   For Lee was beating a wild retreat;
The British were riding the Yankee down,
   And panic was pressing on flying feet.

Galloping down like a hurricane
   Washington rode with his sword swung high,
Mighty as he of the Trojan plain
   Fired by a courage from the sky.

"Halt, and stand to your guns!" he cried.
   And a bombardier made swift reply.
Wheeling his cannon into the tide,
   He fell 'neath the shot of a foeman high.

Molly Pitcher sprang to his side,
   Fired as she saw her husband do.
Telling the king in his stubborn pride
   Women like men to their homes are true.

Washington rode from the bloody fray
   Up to the gun that a woman manned.
"Molly Pitcher, you saved the day,"
   He said, as he gave her a hero's hand.

He named her sergeant with manly praise,
  While her war-brown face was wet with tears—
A woman has ever a woman's ways,
  And the army was wild with cheers.

THREE HUNDRED THOUSAND MORE
James Sloane Gibbons (1810–1892)

We are coming, Father Abraham, three hundred thousand more,
From Mississippi's winding stream and from New England's
    shore;
We leave our plows and workshops, our wives and children dear,
With hearts too full for utterance, with but a silent tear;
We dare not look behind us, but steadfastly before;
We are coming, Father Abraham, three hundred thousand more!

If you look across the hilltops that meet the northern sky,
Long moving lines of rising dust your vision may descry;
And now the wind, an instant, tears the cloudy veil aside,
And floats aloft our spangled flag, in glory and in pride,
And bayonets in the sunlight gleam, and bands brave music pour;
We are coming, Father Abraham, three hundred thousand more!

If you look all up our valleys where the growing harvests shine,
You may see our sturdy farmer boys fast forming into line;
And children from their mothers' knees are pulling at the weeds,
And learning how to reap and sow against their country's needs.
And a farewell group stands weeping at every cottage door;
We are coming, Father Abraham, three hundred thousand more!

NEW ENGLAND'S CHEVY CHASE

April 19, 1775

Edward Everett Hale (1822–1909)

'Twas the dead of the night. By the pineknot's red light
  Brooks lay, half asleep, when he heard the alarm—
Only this, and no more, from a voice at the door:
  "The Red Coats are out, and have passed Phips's farm."

Brooks was booted and spurred; he said never a word:
  Took his horn from its peg, and his gun from the rack;
To the cold midnight air he led out his white mare,
  Strapped the girths and the bridle, and sprang to her back.

Up the North County road at her full pace she strode,
  Till Brooks reined her up at John Tarbell's to say,
"We have got the alarm—they have left Phips's farm;
  You rouse the East Precinct, and I'll go this way."

John called his hired man, and they harnessed the span;
  They roused Abram Garfield, and Abram called me:
"Turn out right away; let no minuteman stay;
  The Redcoats have landed at Phips's," says he.

By the Powder House Green seven others fell in;
  At Nahum's the men from the Sawmill came down;
So that when Jabez Bland gave the word of command,
And said, "Forward, march!" there marched forward THE TOWN.

Parson Wilderspin stood by the side of the road,
   And he took off his hat, and he said, "Let us pray!
O Lord, God of might, let Thine angels of light
   Lead Thy children tonight to the glories of day!
And let Thy stars fight all the foes of the Right
   As the stars fought of old against Sisera."

And from heaven's high arch those stars blessed our march,
   Till the last of them faded in twilight away;
And with morning's bright beam, by the banks of the stream
   Half the county marched in, and we heard Davis say:

"On the King's own highway I may travel all day,
   And no man hath warrant to stop me," says he;
"I've no man that's afraid, and I'll march at their head."
   Then he turned to the boys, "Forward, march! Follow me."

And we marched as he said, and the Fifer he played
   The old "White Cockade," and he played it right well.
We saw Davis fall dead, but no man was afraid;
   That bridge we'd have had, though a thousand men fell.

This opened the play, and it lasted all day.
   We made Concord too hot for the Redcoats to stay;
Down the Lexington way we stormed, black, white, and gray
   We were first in the feast, and were last in the fray.

They would turn in dismay, as red wolves turn at bay.
   They leveled, they fired, they charged up the road.
Cephas Willard fell dead; he was shot in the head
   As he knelt by Aunt Prudence's well sweep to load.

John Danforth was hit just in Lexington Street,
   John Bridge at that lane where you cross Beaver Falls,
And Winch and the Snows just above John Munroe's—
   Swept away by one swoop of the big cannonballs.

I took Bridge on my knee, but he said, "Don't mind me;
Fill your horn from mine—let me lie where I be.
Our fathers," says he, "that their sons might be free,
Left their king on his throne, and came over the sea;
And that man is a knave, or a fool who, to save
His life for a minute, would live like a slave."

Well, all would not do! There were men good as new—
   From Rumford, from Saugus, from towns far away—
Who filled up quick and well for each soldier that fell;
   And we drove them, and drove them, and drove them, all day.
We knew, every one, it was war that begun,
When that morning's marching was only half done.

In the hazy twilight, at the coming of night,
   I crowded three buckshot and one bullet down.
'Twas my last charge of lead; and I aimed her and said,
   "Good luck to you, lobsters, in old Boston Town."

In a barn at Milk Row, Ephraim Bates and Munroe,
   And Baker, and Abram, and I made a bed.
We had mighty sore feet, and we'd nothing to eat;
   But we'd driven the Redcoats, and Amos, he said:
"It's the first time," says he, "that it's happened to me
   To march to the sea by this road where we've come;
But confound this whole day, but we'd all of us say
   We'd rather have spent it this way than to home."

[113]

The hunt had begun with the dawn of the sun,
    And night saw the wolf driven back to his den.
And never since then, in the memory of men,
    Has the Old Bay State seen such a hunting again.

LITTLE GIFFEN
Francis Orray Ticknor

Out of the focal and foremost fire,
Out of the hospital walls as dire,
Smitten of grapeshot and gangrene
(Eighteenth battle and *he* sixteen!)
Spectre such as you seldom see,
Little Giffen of Tennessee.

"Take him and welcome!" the surgeon said;
"Little the doctor can help the dead!"
So we took him and brought him where
The balm was sweet on the summer air;
And we laid him down on a wholesome bed—
Utter Lazarus, heel to head!

And we watched the war with bated breath—
Skeleton Boy against skeleton Death.
Months of torture, how many such!
Weary weeks of the stick and crutch;
And still a glint in the steel-blue eye
Told of a spirit that would not die—

And didn't. Nay, more! in death's despite
The crippled skeleton learned to write.
"Dear Mother," at first, of course; and then,
"Dear Captain," inquiring about "the men."
Captain's answer, "Of eighty-and-five,

Giffen and I are left alive."

Word of gloom from the war, one day:
"Johnston's pressed at the front, they say!"
Little Giffen was up and away;
A tear—his first—as he bade good-bye,
Dimmed the glint of his steel-blue eye.
"I'll write, if spared." There was news of the fight;
But none of Giffen—He did not write.

I sometimes fancy that, were I king
Of the princely Knights of the Golden Ring
With the song of the minstrel in mine ear,
And the tender legend that trembles here,
I'd give the best on his bended knee,
The whitest soul of my chivalry,
For Little Giffen of Tennessee.

JOHN PAUL JONES

September 23, 1779

Walt Whitman (1819–1892)

Would you hear of an old-time sea fight?
Would you hear who won by the light of the moon and stars?
List to the yarn as my grandmother's father the sailor told it to me.

Our foe was no sulk in his ship I tell you (said he,)
His was the surly English pluck, and there is no tougher or
    truer, and never was, and never will be;
Along the lower'd eve he came horribly raking at us.
We closed with him, the yards entangled, the cannon touched.
My captain lashed fast with his own hands.

We had received some eighteen pound shots under the water,
On the lower gun deck two large pieces had burst at the first
    fire, killing all around and blowing up overhead.

Fighting at sundown, fighting at dark,
Ten o'clock at night, the full moon well up, our leaks on the
    gain, and five feet of water reported,
The master-at-arms loosing the prisoners confined in the after
    hold to give them a chance for themselves.

The transit to and from the magazine is now stopped by the
    sentinels,
They see so many strange faces they do not know whom to trust.

Our frigate takes fire,
The other asks if we demand quarter?
If our colors are struck and the fighting done?

Now I laugh content, for I hear the voice of my little captain,
We have not struck, he composedly cries, *we have just begun
our part of the fighting.*

Only three guns are in use,
One is directed by the captain himself against the enemy's main-
mast,
Two well-serv'd with grape and canister silence his musketry
and clear his decks.

The tops alone second the fire of this little battery, especially
the maintop,
They hold out bravely during the whole of the action.
Not a moment's cease,
The leaks gain fast on the pumps, the fire eats toward the powder
magazine.

One of the pumps has been shot away, it is generally thought
we are sinking.

Serene stands the little captain,
He is not hurried, his voice is neither high nor low,
His eyes give more light to us than our battle lanterns.

Toward twelve there in the beams of the moon they surrender
to us.

BARBARA FRIETCHIE
John Greenleaf Whittier (1807–1892)

Up from the meadows rich with corn,
Clear in the cool September morn,

The clustered spires of Frederick stand
Green-walled by the hills of Maryland.

Round about them orchards sweep,
Apple and peach-tree fruited deep,

Fair as a garden of the Lord
To the eyes of the famished rebel horde,

On that pleasant morn of the early fall
When Lee marched over the mountain wall;

Over the mountains winding down,
Horse and foot, into Frederick town.

Forty flags with their silver stars,
Forty flags with their crimson bars,

Flapped in the morning wind: the sun
Of noon looked down, and saw not one.

Up rose old Barbara Frietchie then,
Bowed with her fourscore years and ten;

Bravest of all in Frederick town,
She took up the flag the men hauled down;

In her attic window the staff she set,
To show that one heart was loyal yet.

Up the street came the rebel tread,
Stonewall Jackson riding ahead.

Under his slouched hat left and right
He glanced; the old flag met his sight.

"Halt!"—the dust-brown ranks stood fast.
"Fire!"—out blazed the rifle blast.

It shivered the window, pane and sash;
It rent the banner with seam and gash.

Quick, as it fell, from the broken staff
Dame Barbara snatched the silken scarf.

She leaned far out on the windowsill,
And shook it forth with a royal will.

"Shoot, if you must, this old gray head,
But spare your country's flag," she said.

A shade of sadness, a blush of shame,
Over the face of the leader came;

The nobler nature within him stirred
To life at the woman's deed and word;

"Who touches a hair of yon gray head
Dies like a dog! March on!" he said.

All day long through Frederick street
Sounded the tread of marching feet:

All day long that free flag tost
Over the heads of the rebel host.

Ever its torn folds rose and fell
On the loyal winds that loved it well;

And through the hill-gaps sunset light
Shone over it with a warm good-night.

Barbara Frietchie's work is o'er,
And the Rebel rides on his raids no more.

Honor to her! and let a tear
Fall, for her sake, on Stonewall's bier.

Over Barbara Frietchie's grave,
Flag of Freedom and Union, wave!

Peace and order and beauty draw
Round thy symbol of light and law;

And ever the stars above look down
On thy stars below in Frederick town!

LINCOLN, THE MAN OF THE PEOPLE
Edwin Markham

When the Norn Mother saw the Whirlwind Hour
Greatening and darkening as it hurried on,
She left the Heaven of Heroes and came down
To make a man to meet the mortal need.
She took the tired clay of the common road—
Clay warm yet with the genial heat of earth,
Dashed through it all a strain of prophecy;
Tempered the heap with thrill of human tears;
Then mixed a laughter with the serious stuff.
Into the shape she breathed a flame to light
That tender, tragic, ever-changing face;
And laid on him a sense of the Mystic Powers,
Moving—all hushed—behind the mortal veil.
Here was a man to hold against the world,
A man to match the mountains and the sea.

The color of the ground was in him, the red earth;
The smack and tang of elemental things:
The rectitude and patience of the cliff;
The good will of the rain that loves all leaves;
The friendly welcome of the wayside well;
The courage of the bird that dares the sea;
The gladness of the wind that shakes the corn;
The pity of the snow that hides all scars;
The secrecy of streams that make their way
Under the mountain to the rifted rock;

The tolerance and equity of light
That gives as freely to the shrinking flower
As to the great oak flaring to the wind—
To the grave's low hill as to the Matterhorn
That shoulders out the sky. Sprung from the West,
He drank the valorous youth of a new world.
The strength of virgin forests braced his mind,
The hush of spacious prairies stilled his soul.
His words were oaks in acorns; and this thoughts
Were roots that firmly gripped the granite truth.

Up from the log cabin to the Capitol,
One fire was on his spirit, one resolve—
To send the keen ax to the root of wrong,
Clearing a free way for the feet of God,
The eyes of conscience testing every stroke,
To make his deed the measure of a man.
He built the rail pile as he built the State,
Pouring his splendid strength through every blow;
The grip that swung the ax in Illinois
Was on the pen that set the people free.

So came the Captain with the mighty heart,
And when the judgment thunders split the house,
Wrenching the rafters from their ancient rest,
He held the ridgepole up, and spiked again
The rafters of the Home. He held his place—
Held the long purpose like a growing tree—
Held on through blame and faltered not at praise.
And when he fell in whirlwind, he went down
As when a lordly cedar, green with boughs,
Goes down with a great shout upon the hills,
And leaves a lonely place against the sky.

[123]

From LINCOLN
John Gould Fletcher

There was a darkness in this man; an immense and hollow dark-
    ness,
Of which we may not speak, nor share with him, nor enter;
A darkness through which strong roots stretched downwards
    into the earth
Towards old things;
Towards the herdman-kings who walked the earth and spoke
    with God,
Towards the wanderers who sought for they knew not what,
    and found their goal at last;
Towards the men who waited, only waited patiently when all
    seemed lost,
Many bitter winters of defeat;
Down to the granite of patience
These roots swept, knotted fibrous roots, prying, piercing, seek-
    ing,
And drew from the living rock and the living waters about it
The red sap to carry upwards to the sun.

Not proud, but humble,
Only to serve and pass on, to endure to the end through service;
For the ax is laid at the root of the trees, and all that bring not
    forth good fruit
Shall be cut down on the day to come and cast into the fire.

There is silence abroad in the land today,

And in the hearts of men, a deep and anxious silence;
And, because we are still at last, those bronze lips slowly open,
Those hollow and weary eyes take on a gleam of light.

*　　*　　*　　*

The clamor of cannon dies down, the furnace-mouth of the battle
　　is silent.
The midwinter sun dips and descends, the earth takes on afresh
　　its bright colors.

But he whom we mocked and obeyed not, he whom we scorned
　　and mistrusted,
He has descended, like a god, to his rest.

Over the uproar of cities,
Over the million intricate threads of life wavering and crossing,
In the midst of problems we know not, tangling, perplexing,
　　ensnaring,
Rises one white tomb alone.
Beam over it, stars.
Wrap it round, stripes—stripes red for the pain that he bore for
　　you—
Enfold it forever, O flag, rent, soiled, but repaired through your
　　anguish;
Long as you keep him there safe, the nations shall bow to your
　　law.

Strew over him flowers:
Blue forget-me-nots from the north, and the bright pink arbutus
From the east, and from the west rich orange blossoms,
But from the heart of the land take the passionflower;

[125]

Rayed, violet, dim,
With the nails that pierced, the cross that he bore and the circlet,
And beside it there lay also one lonely snow-white magnolia,
Bitter for remembrance of the healing which has passed.

O CAPTAIN! MY CAPTAIN!

Written on the death of Abraham Lincoln

Walt Whitman (1819–1892)

O Captain! my Captain! our fearful trip is done;
The ship has weather'd every rack, the prize we sought is won;
The port is near, the bells I hear, the people all exulting,
While follow eyes the steady keel, the vessel grim and daring;
  But O heart! heart! heart!
    O the bleeding drops of red,
      Where on the deck my Captain lies,
        Fallen cold and dead.

O Captain! my Captain! rise up and hear the bells;
Rise up—for you the flag is flung—for you the bugle trills;
For you bouquets and ribbon'd wreaths—for you the shores
        a-crowding;
For you they call, the swaying mass, their eager faces turning;
  Here Captain! dear father!
    This arm beneath your head!
      It is some dream that on the deck,
        You've fallen cold and dead.

My Captain does not answer, his lips are pale and still;
My father does not feel my arm, he has no pulse nor will;
The ship is anchor'd safe and sound, its voyage closed and done,
From fearful trip, the victor ship comes in with object won;
  Exult O shores, and ring, O bells!
    But I, with mournful tread,
      Walk the deck my Captain lies,
        Fallen cold and dead.

SHILOH

A Requiem (April, 1862)

Herman Melville (1819–1891)

Skimming lightly, wheeling still,
   The swallows fly low
Over the field in clouded days,
   The forest field of Shiloh—
Over the field where April rain
Solaced the parched one stretched in pain
Through the pause of night
That followed the Sunday fight
   Around the church of Shiloh—
The church so lone, the log-built one,
That echoed to many a parting groan
   And natural prayer
   Of dying foemen mingled there—
Foemen at morn, but friends at eve—
   Fame or country least their care:
(What like a bullet can undeceive!)
   But now they lie low,
While over them the swallows skim,
   And all is hushed at Shiloh.

THE OLD FLAG
H. C. Bunner (1851–1896)

Off with your hat as the flag goes by!
   And let the heart have its say;
You're man enough for a tear in your eye
   That you will not wipe away.

You're man enough for a thrill that goes
   To your very finger tips;
Ay! the lump just then in your throat that rose
   Spoke more than your parted lips.

Lift up the boy on your shoulder high,
   And show him the faded shred;
Those stripes would be red as the sunset sky
   If death could have dyed them red.

Off with your hat as the flag goes by!
   Uncover the youngster's head;
Teach him to hold it holy and high
   For the sake of its sacred dead.

FARRAGUT

Mobile Bay, August 5, 1864

William Tucker Meredith (1830–?)

Farragut, Farragut,
    Old Heart of Oak,
Daring Dave Farragut.
    Thunderbolt stroke,
Watches the hoary mist
    Lift from the bay,
Till his flag, glory-kissed,
    Greets the young day.

Far, by gray Morgan's walls,
    Looms the black fleet.
Hark, deck to rampart calls
    With the drums' beat!
Buoy your chains overboard,
    While the steam hums;
Men! to the battlement,
    Farragut comes.

See, as the hurricane
    Hurtles in wrath
Squadrons of clouds amain
    Back from its path!
Back to the parapet,
    To the gun's lips,

Thunderbolt Farragut
　　Hurls the black ships.

Now through the battle's roar
　　Clear the boy sings,
"By the mark fathoms four,"
　　While his lead swings.
Steady the wheelmen five
　　"Nor' by East keep her,"
"Steady," but two alive:
　　How the shells sweep her!

Lashed to the mast that sways
　　Over red decks,
Over the flame that plays
　　Round the torn wrecks,
Over the dying lips
　　Framed for a cheer,
Farragut leads his ships,
　　Guides the line clear.

On by heights cannon-browed,
　　While the spars quiver;
Onward still flames the cloud
　　Where the hulks shiver.
See, yon fort's star is set,
　　Storm and fire past.
Cheer him, lads—Farragut,
　　Lashed to the mast!

Oh! while Atlantic's breast
　　Bears a white sail,

While the Gulf's towering crest
        Tops a green vale,
Men thy bold deeds shall tell,
        Old Heart of Oak,
Daring Dave Farragut,
        Thunderbolt stroke!

ATLANTIC CHARTER: 1942
Francis Brett Young

What were you carrying, Pilgrims, Pilgrims?
What did you carry beyond the sea?
We carried the Book, we carried the Sword,
A steadfast heart in the fear of the Lord,
And a living faith in His plighted word
That all men should be free.

What were your memories, Pilgrims, Pilgrims?
What of the dreams you bore away?
We carried the songs our fathers sung
By the hearths of home when they were young,
And the comely words of the mother-tongue
In which they learnt to pray.

What did you find there, Pilgrims, Pilgrims?
What did you find beyond the waves?
A stubborn land and a barren shore,
Hunger and want and sickness sore:
All these we found and gladly bore
Rather than be slaves.

How did you fare there, Pilgrims, Pilgrims?
What did you build in that stubborn land?
We felled the forest and tilled the sod
Of a continent no man had trod

And we established there, in the Grace of God,
The rights whereby we stand.

What are you bringing us, Pilgrims, Pilgrims?
Bringing us back in this bitter day?
    The selfsame things we carried away:
    The Book, the Sword,
    The fear of the Lord,
    And the boons our fathers dearly bought:
    Freedom of Worship, Speech and Thought,
    Freedom from Want, Freedom from Fear,
    The liberties we hold most dear,
    And who shall say us Nay?

V

WITH MALICE TOWARD NONE

WITH MALICE TOWARD NONE

From Abraham Lincoln's Second Inaugural Address, 1865

. . . With malice toward none; with charity for all; with firmness in the right, as God gives us to see the right, let us strive on to finish the work we are in; to bind up the nation's wounds; to care for him who shall have borne the battle, and for his widow and his orphan—to do all which may achieve and cherish a just and lasting peace among ourselves, and with all nations.

VICTOR AND VANQUISHED

The Surrender of General Robert E. Lee, 1865
from *The Personal Memoirs of U. S. Grant*

Ulysses S. Grant

What General Lee's feelings were I do not know. As he was a man of much dignity with an impassive face, it was impossible to say whether he felt inwardly glad that the end had finally come, or felt sad over the result, and was too manly to show it. Whatever his feelings, they were entirely concealed from my observation; but my own feelings, which had been quite jubilant on the receipt of his letter, were sad and depressed. I felt like anything rather than rejoicing at the downfall of a foe who had fought so long and valiantly, and had suffered so much for a cause, though that cause was, I believe, one of the worst for which a people ever fought, and one for which there was the least excuse. I do not question, however, the sincerity of the great mass of those who were opposed to us.

*   *   *   *

We soon fell into a conversation about old army times. He remarked that he remembered me very well in the old army; and I told him that as a matter of course I remembered him perfectly, but from the difference in our rank and years (there being about sixteen years' difference in our ages), I had thought it very likely that I had not attracted his attention sufficiently to be remembered by him after such a long interval. Our conversation grew so pleasant that I almost forgot the object of our meeting, and said that he had asked for this interview for the purpose of getting from me the terms I proposed to give his army. I said that I meant merely that his army should lay down their arms, not to take them up again during the continuance of the war unless duly and properly exchanged. . . .

When I put my pen to the paper (to write the surrender terms), . . . the thought occurred to me that the officers (of the Confederacy) had their own private horses and effects, which were important to them, but of no value to us; also, it would be an unnecessary humiliation to call upon them to deliver their side arms. . . .

I took it that most of the men in the (Confederate) ranks were small farmers. The whole country had been so raided by the two armies that it was doubtful whether they would be able to put in a crop to carry themselves and their families through the next winter without the aid of the horses they were then riding. The United States did not want them, and I would, therefore, instruct the officers I left behind to receive the paroles of his troops to let every man of the Confederate army who claimed to own a horse or mule take the animal to his home . . .

General Lee . . . remarked that his army was in a very bad condition for want of food, and that they were without forage; that his men had been living for some days on parched corn exclusively, and that he would have to ask me for rations and forage. I told him "certainly,". . . and I authorized him to send his own commissary and quartermaster to Appomattox Station, two or three miles away, where he could have, out of the trains we had stopped, all the provisions he wanted. . . . Lee and I then separated as cordially as we had met, he returning to his own lines, and all went into bivouac for the night at Appomattox.

"DIXIE"

On April 10, 1865, the city of Washington learned of Lee's surrender. Hysterical with joy, a crowd surged to the White House and demanded a speech from President Abraham Lincoln. With his usual dry humor, tempered now with compassion for a man he held in high respect, the President answered:

> "I am very greatly rejoiced to find that an occasion has occurred so pleasurable that the people cannot restrain themselves. I suppose that arrangements are being made for some sort of formal demonstration, this, or perhaps tomorrow night. If there should be such a demonstration, I, of course, will be called upon to respond, and I shall have nothing to say if you dribble it all out of me before. I see you have a band of music with you. I propose closing up this interview by the band performing a particular tune which I will name. Before this is done, however, I wish to mention one or two little circumstances connected with it. I have always thought 'Dixie' one of the best tunes I have ever heard. Our adversaries over the way attempted to appropriate it, but I insisted yesterday that we fairly captured it. I presented the opinion to the Attorney General, and he gave it as his legal opinion that it is our lawful prize. I now request the band to favor me with its performance."

THE BLUE AND THE GRAY
Francis Miles Finch (1827–1907)

By the flow of the inland river,
　　Whence the fleets of iron have fled,
Where the blades of the grave-grass quiver,
　　Asleep are the ranks of the dead—
Under the sod and the dew,
　　Waiting the Judgment Day—
Under the one, the Blue;
　　Under the other, the Gray.

These in the robings of glory,
　　Those in the gloom of defeat,
All with the Battle-blood gory,
　　In the dusk of eternity meet—
Under the sod and the dew,
　　Waiting the Judgment Day—
Under the laurel, the Blue;
　　Under the willow, the Gray.

From the silence of sorrowful hours
　　The desolate mourners go,
Lovingly laden with flowers,
　　Alike for the friend and the foe—
Under the sod and the dew,
　　Waiting the Judgment Day—
Under the roses, the Blue;
　　Under the lilies, the Gray.

So, with an equal splendor
    The morning sunrays fall,
With a touch impartially tender,
    On the blossoms blooming for all—
Under the sod and the dew,
    Waiting the Judgment Day—
Broidered with gold, the Blue;
    Mellowed with gold, the Gray.

So, when the summer calleth,
    On forest and field of grain,
With an equal murmur falleth
    The cooling drip of the rain—
Under the sod and the dew,
    Waiting the Judgment Day—
Wet with the rain, the Blue;
    Wet with the rain, the Gray.

Sadly, but not with upbraiding,
    The generous deed was done.
In the storm of the years that are fading
    No braver battle was won—
Under the sod and the dew,
    Waiting the Judgment Day;
Under the blossoms, the Blue;
    Under the garlands, the Gray.

No more shall the war cry sever,
    Or the winding rivers be red:
They banish our anger forever
    When they laurel the graves of our dead!
Under the sod and the dew,

Waiting the Judgment Day—
Love and tears for the Blue;
Tears and love for the Gray.

A GERMAN IMMIGRANT

(When asked why he had chosen to come to America to live)

During World War I, when I was a boy, we were all hungry.
I do not remember a full stomach in that whole time. Then the
war was over, and the Americans came with kettles of hot food
to feed the children. Later, I promised myself I would live in
the country that fed its enemies.

I am ready to say to every human being, "Thou art my brother,"
and to offer him the hand of concord and amity.

THOMAS JEFFERSON

AMERICA GREETS AN ALIEN
Author Unknown

Hail, guest! We ask not what thou art.
If friend, we greet thee hand and heart;
If stranger, such no longer be;
If foe, our love shall conquer thee.

When Kansas and Colorado have a quarrel over the water in the Arkansas River they don't call out the National Guard in each State and go to war over it. They bring a suit in the Supreme Court of the United States and abide by the decision. There isn't a reason in the world why we cannot do that internationally.

HARRY S. TRUMAN, 1945

THE NEW COLOSSUS

Written in 1883. The Statue of Liberty was unveiled in 1886

Emma Lazarus

Not like the brazen giant of Greek fame,
With conquering limbs astride from land to land;
Here at our sea-washed, sunset gates shall stand
A mighty woman with a torch, whose flame
Is the imprisoned lightning, and her name
Mother of Exiles. From her beacon-hand
Glows worldwide welcome; her mild eyes command
The air-bridged harbor that twin cities frame.
"Keep, ancient lands, your storied pomp!" cries she
With silent lips. "Give me your tired, your poor,
Your huddled masses yearning to breathe free,
The wretched refuse of your teeming shore.
Send these, the homeless, tempest-tossed to me,
I lift my lamp beside the golden door!"

In the field of world policy, I would dedicate this nation to the
policy of the good neighbor.
FRANKLIN D. ROOSEVELT, IN HIS FIRST INAUGURAL ADDRESS,
MARCH 4, 1933

VI

LEST WE FORGET

E PLURIBUS

UNUM

MEMORIAL DAY
William E. Brooks

I heard a cry in the night from a far-flung host,
From a host that sleeps through the years the last long sleep,
By the Meuse, by the Marne, in the Argonne's shattered wood,
In a thousand rose-thronged churchyards through our land.
Sleep! Do they sleep? I know I heard their cry,
Shrilling along the night like a trumpet blast:

"We died," they cried, "for a dream. Have ye forgot?
We dreamed of a world reborn whence wars had fled,
Where swords were broken in pieces and guns were rust,
Where the poor man dwelt in quiet, the rich in peace,
And children played in the streets, joyous and free.
We thought we could sleep content in a task well done;
But the rumble of guns rolls over us, iron upon iron
Sounds from the forge where are fashioned guns anew;

"New fleets spring up in new seas, and under the wave
Stealthy new terrors swarm, with emboweled death.
Fresh cries of hate ring out loud from the demagogue's throat,
While greed reaches out afresh to grasp new lands.
Have we died in vain? Is our dream denied?
You men who live on the earth we bought with our woe,
Will ye stand idly by while they shape new wars,
Or will ye rise, who are strong, to fulfill our dream,
To silence the demagogue's voice, to crush the fools

Who play with bloodstained toys that crowd new graves?
We call, we call in the night, will ye hear and heed?"

In the name of our dead will we hear? Will we grant them sleep?

THESE ARE THE TIMES
THAT TRY MEN'S SOULS

from *"The American Crisis"*

Thomas Paine

♜

These are the times that try men's souls. The summer soldier and the sunshine patriot will, in this crisis, shrink from the service of their country; but he that stands it *now,* deserves the love and thanks of man and woman. Tyranny, like hell, is not easily conquered; yet we have this consolation with us, that the harder the conflict, the more glorious the triumph. What we obtain too cheap, we esteem too lightly; it is dearness only that gives everything its value. Heaven knows how to put a proper price upon its goods; and it would be strange, indeed, if so celestial an article as FREEDOM should not be highly rated.

Our Constitution is in actual operation; everything appears to promise that it will last; but in this world nothing is certain but death and taxes.

BENJAMIN FRANKLIN, 1706–1790

GEORGE WASHINGTON
TO THE AMERICAN TROOPS
BEFORE THE BATTLE OF LONG ISLAND

The time is now near at hand which must probably determine whether Americans are to be freemen or slaves; whether they are to have any property they can call their own; whether their houses and farms are to be pillaged and destroyed, and themselves consigned to a state of wretchedness from which no human efforts will deliver them. The fate of unborn millions will now depend, under God, on the courage and conduct of this army. Our cruel and unrelenting enemy leaves us only the choice of a brave resistance, or the most abject submission. We have, therefore, to resolve to conquer or to die.

One may live as a conqueror, a king, or a magistrate; but he must die as a man.

DANIEL WEBSTER, 1782–1852

[151]

ARSENALS AND FORTS

from *"The Arsenal at Springfield"*

Henry Wadsworth Longfellow (1807–1882)

Were half the power that fills the world with terror,
Were half the wealth, bestowed on camps and courts,
Given to redeem the human mind from error,
There were no need of arsenals nor forts.

God grants liberty only to those who love it, and are always
ready to guard and defend it.

DANIEL WEBSTER, 1782–1852

EXCERPT FROM LINCOLN'S SPEECH ON LEAVING SPRINGFIELD, ILLINOIS, TO ASSUME THE PRESIDENCY OF THE UNITED STATES

. . . I have tried to inquire what great principle or ideal is it that has kept this Union so long together? And I believe that it was not the mere matter of separation of the colonies from the motherland, but that sentiment in the Declaration of Independence which gave liberty to the people of this country and hope to all the world. This sentiment was the fulfillment of an ancient dream, which men have held through all time, that they might one day shake off their chains and find freedom in the brotherhood of life. We gained democracy, and now there is the question whether it is fit to survive. Perhaps we have come to the dreadful day of awakening, and the dream is ended. If so, I am afraid it must be ended forever. I cannot believe that ever again will men have the opportunity we have had. Perhaps we should admit that and concede that our ideals of liberty and equality are decadent and doomed. I have heard of an Eastern monarch who once charged his wise men to invent him a sentence which would be true and appropriate in all times and situations. They presented him the words, "And this too shall pass away." That is a comforting thought in time of affliction—"And this too shall pass away." And yet—let us believe that it is not true! Let us live to prove that we can cultivate the natural world that is about us, and the intellectual and moral world that is within us, so that we may secure an individual, social, and political prosperity, whose course shall be forward, and which, while the earth endures, shall not pass away.

ADDRESS

Delivered at Gettysburg, Pennsylvania,
November 19, 1863

President Abraham Lincoln

Fourscore and seven years ago our fathers brought forth on this continent a new nation, conceived in liberty, and dedicated to the proposition that all men are created equal.

Now we are engaged in a great civil war, testing whether that nation, or any nation so conceived and so dedicated, can long endure. We are met on a great battlefield of that war. We have come to dedicate a portion of that field as a final resting place for those who here gave their lives that that nation might live. It is altogether fitting and proper that we should do this.

But in a larger sense we cannot dedicate, we cannot consecrate, we cannot hallow this ground. The brave men, living and dead, who struggled here, have consecrated it far above our poor power to add or detract. The world will little note, nor long remember, what we say here, but it can never forget what they did here. It is for us, the living, rather to be dedicated here to the unfinished work which they who fought here have thus far so nobly advanced. It is rather for us to be here dedicated to the great task remaining before us, that from these honored dead we take increased devotion to that cause for which they gave the last full measure of devotion; that we here highly resolve that these dead shall not have died in vain; that this nation, under God, shall have a new birth of freedom; and that government of the people, by the people, for the people, shall not perish from the earth.

A NATION'S STRENGTH
Ralph Waldo Emerson (1803–1882)

What makes a nation's pillars high
  And its foundations strong?
What makes it mighty to defy
  The foes that round it throng?

It is not gold. Its kingdoms grand
  Go down in battle shock;
Its shafts are laid on sinking sand,
Not on abiding rock.

Is it the sword? Ask the red dust
  Of empires passed away;
The blood has turned their stones to rust,
  Their glory to decay.

And is it pride? Ah, that bright crown
  Has seemed to nations sweet;
But God has struck its luster down
  In ashes at his feet.

Not gold but only men can make
  A people great and strong;
Men who for truth and honor's sake
  Stand fast and suffer long.

Brave men who work while others sleep,

Who dare while others fly—
They build a nation's pillars deep
And lift them to the sky.

Laws too gentle are seldom obeyed; too severe, seldom executed.
BENJAMIN FRANKLIN

THE LAND WHERE HATE SHOULD DIE
Denis A. McCarthy

This is the land where hate should die—
  No feuds of faith, no spleen of race,
No darkly brooding fear should try
  Beneath our flag to find a place.
Lo! every people here has sent
  Its sons to answer freedom's call;
Their lifeblood is the strong cement
  That builds and binds the nation's wall.

This is the land where hate should die—
  Though dear to me my faith and shrine,
I serve my country well when I
  Respect beliefs that are not mine.
He little loves his land who'd cast
  Upon his neighbor's word a doubt,
Or cite the wrongs of ages past
  From present rights to bar him out.

This is the land where hate should die—
  This is the land where strife should cease,
Where foul, suspicious fear should fly
  Before our flag of light and peace.
Then let us purge from poisoned thought
  That service to the State we give,
And so be worthy as we ought
  Of this great Land in which we live!

From AD PATRIAM
William Dudley Foulke (1848–1935)

                                          Land of my heart,
What future is before thee? Shall it be
To lie at ease, content with thy bright past,
Heedless of all the world, till idleness
Relax thy limbs, and swollen with wealth and pride
Thou shalt abandon justice and the poor?
Or shalt thou, reawakened, scatter wide
The glorious tidings of a liberty
That lifts the latch of opportunity
First to thy children—then to all mankind?
Love of my soul—God keep thee strong and pure,
That thou shalt be a fitting messenger
To carry hope to all the sons of men.

Let us remember that revolutions do not always establish freedom.
MILLARD FILLMORE, 1800–1874. THIRTEENTH PRESIDENT OF
                                          THE UNITED STATES

OUR COUNTRY, RIGHT OR WRONG
Carl Schurz (1829–1906)

*German army officer, politician and revolutionist. Fled to the
United States in 1852. Became brigadier general of Union
volunteers during American Civil War.*

🔔

Our country, right or wrong. When right, to be kept right;
when wrong, to be put right.

ONCE TO EVERY MAN AND NATION
from *The Present Crisis*
James Russell Lowell (1819–1891)

🔔

. . . Once to every man and nation comes the moment to decide,
In the strife of Truth with Falsehood, for the good or evil side;
Some great cause, God's new Messiah, offering each the bloom
    or blight,
Parts the goats upon the left hand, and the sheep upon the right,
And the choice goes by forever 'twixt that darkness and that
    light.

Hast thou chosen, O my people, on whose party thou shalt stand,
Ere the Doom from its worn sandals shakes the dust against our
    land?

[159]

Though the cause of Evil prosper, yet 'tis Truth alone is strong,
And, albeit she wander outcast now, I see around her throng
Troops of beautiful, tall angels, to enshield her from all wrong.

Careless seems the great Avenger; history's pages but record
One death-grapple in the darkness 'twixt old systems and the
    Word;
Truth forever on the scaffold, Wrong forever on the throne—
Yet that scaffold sways the future, and behind the dim unknown,
Standeth God within the shadow, keeping watch above his own.

Then to side with Truth is noble when we share her wretched
    crust,
Ere her cause bring fame and profit, and 'tis prosperous to be
    just;
Then it is the brave man chooses, while the coward stands aside,
Doubting in his abject spirit, till his Lord is crucified,
And the multitude make virtue of the faith they had denied.

New occasions teach new duties; Time makes ancient good un-
    couth;
They must upward still, and onward, who would keep abreast of
    Truth;
Lo! before us gleam her campfires! we ourselves must Pilgrims be,
Launch our Mayflower, and steer boldly through the desperate
    winter sea,
Nor attempt the Future's portal with the Past's blood-rusted key.

THE MORAL WARFARE
John Greenleaf Whittier (1807–1892)

When Freedom, on her natal day,
Within her war-rocked cradle lay,
An iron race around her stood,
Baptized her infant brow in blood
And, through the storm which round her swept,
Their constant ward and watching kept.

Then, where our quiet herds repose,
The roar of baleful battle rose,
And brethren of a common tongue
To mortal strife as tigers sprung,
And every gift on Freedom's shrine
Was man for beast, and blood for wine!

Our fathers to their graves have gone;
Their strife is past—their triumph won;
But sterner trials wait the race
Which rises in their honored place—
A moral warfare with the crime
And folly of an evil time.

So let it be. In God's own might
We gird us for the coming fight,
And, strong in Him whose cause is ours
In conflict with unholy powers,
We grasp the weapons He has given,—
The Light, and Truth, and Love of Heaven!

BALLAD OF THE COMMON MAN

For the Jefferson Memorial

Alfred Kreymborg (1883–   )

To him who felt a human sea
Begin to rise for liberty,
    Build, O men, keep building!

To him who raised the human pen
That freed the first American,
    Build, O men, keep building!

For he is in the common star
Of all we live in, all we are
In sons and more sons near and far—
    Build, O men, keep building!

And rear your temple all around
Our common feet and common ground,
Giving our love a common sound—
    Build, O men, keep building!

And let us feel there is no night
Can ever hide the growing light—
The light he saw, the light he spread—
And all our sight, though he is dead—
    Build, O men, keep building!

And even though your labor's done

And the race may rest in Jefferson,
Rise up again, there's more to be done!
Build, O men, keep building!
Keep on building Men!

THE ERRAND IMPERIOUS
Edwin Markham

But harken, my America, my own,
  Great Mother with the hill-flower in your hair!
Diviner is that light you bear alone,
  That dream that keeps your face forever fair.

'Tis yours to bear the World-State in your dream;
  To strike down Mammon and his brazen breed;
To build the Brother-Future, beam on beam—
  Yours, mighty one, to shape the mighty deed.

The àrmed heavens lean down to hear your fame,
  America: rise to your highborn part:
The thunders of the sea are in your name,
  The splendors of the sunrise in your heart.

I AM THE FLAG
Lawrence M. Jones

I am a composite being of all the people of America.
I am the union if you are united.
I am one and indivisible if you are undivided.
I am as strong as the weakest link.
I am an emblem of your country.
I am a symbol of a shadow of the real.
I am a sign pointing to past achievements.
I am a promise of greater things for the future.
I am what you make me.
I am purity if you are pure.
I am bravery if you are brave.
I am loyalty if you are loyal.

* * * * * * *

I am honor if you are honorable.
I am goodness if you are good.
I am hope if you are hopeful.
I am truth if you are true.

* * * * * * *

I am the Constitution.
I am law and order.
I am tolerance or intolerance as you force me to be.
I am liberty as you understand liberty.
I am as a pillar of fire by night, but you must
    provide the fuel.

[165]

* * * * * * *

I march at the head of the column, but you must
carry me on.

* * * * * * *

I stand for greater and more glorious achievement
than can be found in recorded history, but
you must be my inspiration.
I Am the Flag.

THE NECESSITY TO FIGHT

*From President Wilson's address asking Congress to declare war
against Germany, April 2, 1917*

Woodrow Wilson

It is a fearful thing to lead this great and peaceful people into
war, into the most terrible and disastrous of all wars. Civilization
itself seems to be in the balance, but right is more precious than
peace, and we shall fight for the things which we have always
carried nearest our hearts, for democracy, for the right of those
who submit to authority to have a voice in their own government,
for the rights and liberties of small nations, for the universal
dominion of right by such a concert of free peoples as will bring
peace and safety to all nations, and make the world itself at last
free. To such a task we can dedicate our lives, fortunes, everything that we are, everything we have, with the pride of those
who know that the day has come when America is privileged to
spend her blood and her might for the principles that gave her
birth, and the happiness and peace which she has treasured. God
helping her, she can do no other.

IN FLANDERS FIELDS
John McCrae (1872–1918)

In Flanders fields the poppies blow
Between the crosses, row on row,
   That mark our place; and in the sky
   The larks, still bravely singing, fly
Scarce heard amid the guns below.

We are the Dead. Short days ago
We lived, felt dawn, saw sunset glow,
   Loved and were loved, and now we lie
   In Flanders fields.

Take up our quarrel with the foe:
To you from failing hands we throw
   The torch; be yours to hold it high.
   If ye break faith with us who die
We shall not sleep, though poppies grow
   In Flanders fields.

We are provincials no longer. The tragical events of the thirty months of vital turmoil through which we have just passed have made us citizens of the world. There can be no turning back. Our own fortunes as a nation are involved, whether we would have it so or not.

And yet we are not the less Americans on that account. We shall be the more American if we but remain true to the principles in which we have been bred. They are not the principles of a province or of a single continent. We have known and boasted all along that they were the principles of a liberated mankind.

WOODROW WILSON IN HIS SECOND INAUGURAL
ADDRESS, MARCH 4, 1917

Wars are not "acts of God." They are caused by man, by man-made institutions, by the way in which man has organized his society. What man has made, man can change.

Fred M. Vinson
CHIEF JUSTICE OF THE SUPREME COURT
OF THE UNITED STATES

WRITTEN IN A TIME OF CRISIS

(World War II)

Stephen Vincent Benét

It's a long way out of the past and a long way forward.
It's a tough way, too, and there's plenty of trouble in it.
It's a black storm crowding the sky and a cold wind blowing,
Blowing upon us all.
See it and face it. That's the way it is.
That's the way it'll be for a time and a time.
Even the easy may have little ease.
Even the meek may suffer in their meekness.
But we've ridden out storms before, and we'll ride out this one.
Ride it out and get through.
It won't be done by the greedy and the go-easies.
It'll be done by the river of the people,
The mountain of the people, the great plain
Grown to the wheat of the people.
It'll be done by the proud walker, Democracy,
The walker in proud shoes.
Get on your feet, Americans, and say it!
Forget your grievances, wherever you are,
The little yesterday's hates and the last year's discord.
This is your land, this is your independence,
This is the people's cause, the people's might.
Say it and speak it loud, United, free . . .

AMERICA FIRST!
G. Ashton Oldham

Not merely in matters material, but in things of the spirit.

Not merely in science, inventions, motors, and skyscrapers, but also in ideals, principles, character.

Not merely in the calm assumption of rights, but in the glad assumption of duties.

Not flaunting her strength as a giant, but bending in helpfulness over a sick and wounded world like a Good Samaritan.

Not in splendid isolation, but in courageous cooperation.

Not in pride, arrogance, and disdain of other races and peoples, but in sympathy, love, and understanding.

Not in treading again the old, worn, bloody pathway which ends inevitably in chaos and disaster, but in blazing a new trail, along which, please God, other nations will follow, into the New Jerusalem where wars shall be no more.

Some day some nation must take that path—unless we are to lapse once again into utter barbarism—and that honor I covet for my beloved America.

And so, in that spirit and with these hopes, I say with all my heart and soul, "AMERICA FIRST!"

Whatever America hopes to bring to pass in this world must first come to pass in the heart of America.

Dwight D. Eisenhower,
FIRST INAUGURAL ADDRESS, 1953

PRAYER FOR THE NATION
George Washington

May we unite in most humbly offering our prayers and supplications to the Great Lord and Ruler of Nations, and to beseech Him to pardon our national and other transgressions; to enable us all, whether in public or private stations, to perform our several and relative duties properly and punctually; to render our national government a blessing to all the people by constantly being a government of wise, just, and constitutional laws, discreetly and faithfully executed and obeyed; to protect and guide all sovereign nations, and to bless them with good governments, peace and concord; to promote the knowledge and practice of true religion and virtue, and, generally, to grant unto all mankind such a degree of temporal prosperity as He alone knows to be best.

INDEX OF TITLES

[173]

INDEX OF AUTHORS

INDEX OF SUBJECTS

[177]

INDEX OF FIRST LINES OF POEMS

[179]

Mine eyes have seen the glory of the coming of the Lord, 68
My country, 'tis of thee, 62

New England's annoyances you that would know them, 5
Not like the brazen giant of Greek fame, 145
Not merely in matters material, but in things of the spirit, 171

O beautiful for spacious skies, 58
O Captain! my Captain! our fearful trip is done, 127
O Columbia, the gem of the ocean, 60
O miserable me! This is the last, 22
O say, can you see, by the dawn's early light, 64
Off with your hat as the flag goes by!, 129
Oh mother of a mighty race, 10
Once to every man and nation comes the moment to decide, 159
Out of the focal and foremost fire, 115

Scots, wha hae wi' Wallace bled, 71
Shall I begin by saying, 104
She is a rich and rare land;,20
Sing of the brave and the miracles they wrought, 77
Skimming lightly, wheeling still, 128
Soldier and statesman, rarest unison, 97
Stand! the ground's your own, my braves, 103
Sun of the moral world; effulgent source, 19

The land was ours before we were the land's, 31
The Union forever, hurrah, boys, hurrah!, 59
The word of the Lord by night, 42
Then I came back, 30
There is a land, of every land the pride, 21
There was a darkness in this man; an immense and hollow darkness, 124
They are slaves who fear to speak, 46
They set the slave free, striking off his chains, 50
This is the land where hate should die, 157
This royal throne of kings, this scepter'd isle, 23
Thou, too, sail on, O Ship of State!, 9
'Tis fine to see the Old World, and travel up and down, 25
To drumbeat, and heartbeat, 100
To him who felt a human sea, 162
'Twas the dead of the night. By the pineknot's red light, 111

Up from the meadows rich with corn, 119

We are coming, Father Abraham, three hundred thousand more, 110